Cry Hosanna

Cry Hosanna

Edited by Betty Pulkingham
Mimi Farra

HODDER AND STOUGHTON
LONDON SYDNEY AUCKLAND TORONTO

British Library Cataloguing in Publication Data
Cry hosanna
  1. Hymns, English
  I. Pulkingham, Betty
  II. Farra, Mimi
  264'.2   BV350
  ISBN 0 340 25159 X

Contents

1 Songs of Praise and Thanksgiving   11

2 Songs of Worship   51

3 Songs of Hope, Vision and Wholeness   69

4 Songs of the Kingdom   90

5 Songs of Faith and Victory   123

6 Songs of Outreach   146

7 Songs for Children   166

8 Psalms   190

9 Seasonal Songs   219

TOPICAL INDEX   247

WORSHIP LEADERS' GUIDE   250

GUIDE TO THE USE OF ADDITIONAL INSTRUMENTS   253

NOTES FOR GUITARIST/ACCOMPANIST   254

DISCOGRAPHY   255

INDEX OF TITLES AND FIRST LINES   256

Foreword

All over the world Christians are discovering new freedom in praise as they draw together to worship the living God.

> From the fears that long have bound us
> Free our hearts to faith and praise.
> *Harry Emerson Fosdick*

Most of us have been bound at some point to the particular tradition out of which we come, and have needed the Spirit's driving wind to dislodge us from the place where we were 'stuck' and blow us into a larger place – a place of exposure to different cultures, different theologies, different ways of honouring God. Once we have been blown upon and into this larger place, we find an adventure of faith awaiting us, with ever-broadening horizons. The same Spirit who drove Jesus into the wilderness will drive us – his contemporary brothers and sisters – into similar places of exposure, challenge and blessing. It is there that we will learn to cry 'Hosanna'. We will neither croon, nor drone, nor chirp (the world's ways of romanticizing, deadening, or making frivolous the songs of God). But we will sing his praises with a pure heart, fervently, as we have been taught by him to love. From our innermost beings, out of experiences of costly obedience and purifying pain, will well up the Spirit's songs. We will learn to sing them with strong, clear voices, and only such praise as this, plumbed from the depths of God's people, will be able to sustain them through suffering, through persecution, through martyrdom, through the challenges of the last decades of this century.

Cry Hosanna is a collection of 142 songs and hymns which represent God's praising people around the world. It contains many strong hymns from varied traditions. 'People of God', a beautiful Eucharistic hymn from Brazil, is presented here in a new English translation; 'Hymn to the Spirit' originated with the Fountain Trust in England; 'For you are my God' issues from the Roman Catholic renewal in America; 'Jesus is our King' comes from the Post Green Community in England. The international flavour of the songbook is clearly discernible in many of the songs as well: 'Neighbours' from Ghana, 'God is for me' from Sweden, 'A joyful song' from Scotland, '¡Resucitó, resucitó!' from Spain, 'The servant song' from New Zealand.

If this book has a wide geography, it also has a respect for history, incorporating ancient hymns (e.g., 'Come, Holy Ghost') alongside contemporary musical settings of traditional texts (e.g., 'Before the Lord Jehovah's throne', 'O for a thousand tongues'). There are a number of traditional hymns with descants. As in the case of its predecessors, *Sound of Living Waters* and *Fresh Sounds*, the songs in *Cry Hosanna* have been selected because of their proven usefulness in worship, teaching and celebration.

Several new features distinguish the book from its predecessors. Gesture drawings of simple hand and dance movements are included. A Worship Leaders' Guide provides a comprehensive study of ways in which the music may be used. (Which songs, for example, would be useful in a youth service, at a camp or conference, in a liturgical setting, or appropriate for a soloist?) There is a wealth of material here for part-singing, and the enterprising choir director will find suggestions in footnotes for the use of the material, as well as a guide to enhancing the songs through the use of instruments. A special page of instructions for the guitarist/accompanist is included. There is also an expanded topical index.

We, the editors, trust that you will find this a many-faceted and practical songbook for use in contemporary worship.

BETTY PULKINGHAM AND MIMI FARRA
1980

Acknowledgements

The editors are grateful to the following for their help in an advisory capacity during the compilation stages of the songbook: George Mims, Jeanne Harper, Jim Cavnar and Shirley Brown. We also wish to thank Jane Clowe and Sandy Kroondyk (U.S.A), Christine Allan (New Zealand), Pat Allen and Mark Durie (Australia) and Celia Harrisson (England) for their valuable research into song usage in their areas. Our very special appreciation goes to Edward Prebble for his indefatigable work on copyrights and permissions, to Ruth Wieting for preparation of gesture drawings, to Cathleen Morris for the cover design, to Max Dyer, Bill Pulkingham and Sandy Hardyman for reviewing the many music tapes and manuscripts submitted to us, to Shirley Brown for her accompaniments, to Celia Harrisson for copywork, to Louise Jolly for proofreading, to Pat Allen for assistance with the indexes, and to Barbara Gilbert for her expert clerical help. If there is one person whose assistance might be termed 'invaluable', it is Lindsay Treen; for her work in music transcription, manuscript preparation, research correspondence and overall support in seeing the songbook through to publication, we are most grateful.

SECTION 1

SONGS OF PRAISE AND THANKSGIVING

1. Morning Psalm

'St. Owen'

Owen Barker

Sherrell Prebble

With flowing simplicity

1. How beau-ti-ful the morn-ing and the day; My
2. How glo-ri-ous the morn-ing and the day; My
3. How boun-ti-ful the bless-ings that he brings Of

heart a-bounds with mu-sic, my lips can on-ly
heart is still and lis-tens, my soul be-gins to
peace and joy and rap-ture that makes my spi-rit

say: How beau-ti-ful the morn-ing and the day.
pray To him who is the glo-ry of the day.
sing: How boun-ti-ful the bless-ings that he brings.

4. How merciful the workings of his grace,
   Arousing faith and action my soul would never face
   Without his matchless mercy and his grace.

5. How barren was my life before he came,
   Supplying love and healing; I live now to acclaim
   The majesty and wonder of his name.

2. We want to bless you

Lucy Morris
Arr. Betty Pulkingham

Light and fairly fast

Refrain

We want to bless— you; we want to praise—you, Je - sus, our Lord. We want to bless— you; we want to praise you, Je - sus, our Lord.

Fine

1.
2. O
3. The

In—	our	weak - ness
Prince—	of	Peace,	we
free - dom	you	give	is

you are— strong; O Ho - ly Spi - rit,
call on— you; we wor - ship you, praise you,
our de - light; we give— our - selves to

lead ____ us a - long. ____
love ____ you,— too. ____
live ____ in your light. ____

We want to

D.S.

3. Praise ye the Lord

Anon.
Arr. Jeanne Harper

4. Alabaré *

Composer unknown
Arr. Edward Dagnes

With joyful abandon
Intro.

A-la-ba - ré,_____ a-la-ba-

ré,_____ a - la - ba-ré a mi Se - ñor._____ A-la-ba-

ré,_____ a - la-ba - ré,_____ a - la - ba-ré a mi Se -

1.- 3. | *Final ending*

ñor. _____ ñor. _____ 1. John saw the number__of
Juan vió el nú-me-ro__

*Alabaré a mi Señor: I will praise my Lord.

15

16

5. O clap your hands

(Two-part song)

Psalm 47

Wiley Beveridge and Bill Shehee
Arr. Mimi Farra

An effective way to build this two-part song is to sing Part 1 on its own, then Part 2 as far as the asterisk.
Then begin the song with both parts together.

6. Good morning, Jesus

Vs. 1 Unknown
Vs. 2 Rebekah Herold
Vs. 3 Jeff Cothran

Composer unknown
Arr. Betty Pulkingham

Bright and bouncy

1. Good morn - ing, Je - sus, good morn - ing, love;
2. Good morn - ing, Je - sus, good morn - ing, light;
3. Good morn - ing, Je - sus, dear Lord and King;

we know you came from hea - ven a - bove.
you drive the dark - ness a - way like the night.
we want to please you in ev - 'ry - thing,

Your Ho - ly Spi - rit moves like a dove.
I could - n't see but now I walk with your sight.
and so with joy we lift our hearts up and sing,

Good morn - ing, Je - sus, good morn - ing, love.
Good morn - ing, Je - sus, good morn - ing, light.
Good morn - ing, Je - sus, dear Lord and King.

7. Hallelujah song

(two-part song)

Frank Hernandez
Arr. Betty Pulkingham

2. Hallelujah! Hallelujah!
He is King, he is King.
Hallelujah, Jesus is King!
(repeat)

Hallelujah, Jesus is King!

*This is a useful song to help a group have fun together, or to draw together a noisy, scattered group into one activity and one sound.

8. The Lord is present

Gail Cole
Arr. Mimi Farra

Rhythmically, in moderate time

1. The Lord is pres-ent in his sanc-tu-ar - y,

let us praise the
let us sing to the
let us de-light in the
let us love the

Lord! The Lord is pres-ent in his peo - ple gath - ered here,

let us praise the Lord!
let us sing to the Lord!
let us de-light in the Lord!
let us love the Lord!

Praise him,
Sing to him,
De - light in him, de-
Love him,

9. Sing to our Father

Stephen Ball
Jon Wilkes

Lorna Ball

Bold and rhythmical

1. Sing to our Fa-ther, Cre - a - tor and King, who sent his Son, Je - sus, to suf-fer and bring us in - to his fam'-ly. Oh, mag - ni - fy him!
2. Sing to our broth-er, who of him-self poured out life to his peo-ple to see them re - stored.__ Sing to our heal - er and sing to our Lord!
3. Sing to the Spi - rit, __ let us all hear and know that he frees us from sin and from fear to love one an-oth - er, to serve and to care.

Sing, sing, sing, sing, sing to the Lord of

love!
life!
peace!

10. Jubilate Deo

(6 - part round)

Praetorius

Bright and fast

Ju - bi - la - te De - o, ju - bi - la - te De - o, al - le - lu - ia!

11. Hymn of glory

Capo 3 (A)

Charles Christmas
Arr. Charles High

Boldly, with pulsating rhythm

Glo - ry hal - le - lu - jah!

Glo - ry hal - le - lu - jah!

1. Give thanks to our God and let him be praised with
2. His word ev - er true, the Son of his love.
3. Wor - thy the Lamb who was slain for our sins. He
4. Ho - ly, ho - ly the Lord God al - might - y who

sanc - ti - fied hearts and hands that are raised.
Sing, men of earth, to the heav - ens a - bove.
laid down his life, he rose up a - gain.
was, who is, and who is to come. In

Ab(F)	Eb(C)	Bb(G)	C(A)	D.C.

Come, join a song— of praise to our God.
Hon - our and glo - ry be-long to our God.
To us he gives— un-end - ing life.
glo - ry come,— Lord Je - sus, come.

12. Iona Gloria

Anon.

Freely

Part 1

Glo - ri - a, Glo - ri - a, Glo - ri - a, in ex-cel-sis De - o.

Parts 1 & 2

Glo - ri - a, Glo - ri - a, Glo - ri - a, in ex-cel-sis De - o.

Parts 1, 2 & 3

Glo - ri - a, Glo - ri - a, Glo - ri - a, in ex - cel-sis De - o.

A rediscovered Gloria said to be sung by St. Columba and the monks of his Abbey on Iona Island in the years 625 - 640 A.D. It was sung as he left on preaching tours of the mainland. The monks on the shore sang the two upper parts and as the boat embarked, St. Columba and his crew of monks sang the third.

13. Before the Lord Jehovah's throne

Based on Psalm 100
Isaac Watts

'De Tar'
Calvin Hampton

Sustained, with a steady beat

1. Be - fore the Lord Je - ho - vah's throne,
aid
care,

Ye na - tions, bow with sa - cred joy;
Made us of — clay, and formed us — men;
Our souls, and — all — our mor - tal — frame:

Know that the Lord is God a - lone;
And when like wan - d'ring sheep we strayed,
What last - ing hon - ours shall we rear,

*Counter-melody may be played by a solo instrument.

From THREE HYMN TUNES © 1973 Concordia Publishing House, 3558 South Jefferson Ave., St. Louis, MO 63118, U.S.A. Used by permission.

He can cre - ate, and he de - stroy.
He brought us ____ to his fold a - gain.
Al - might - y Ma - ker, to thy name?

1.-4.   *Final ending*

2. His sov'reign power with-out our   A - - - - men.
3. We are his peo - ple, we his

4. We'll crowd thy gates with thankful songs,
   High as the heav'n our voices raise;
   And earth, with her ten thousand tongues,
   Shall fill thy courts with sounding praise.

5. Wide as the world is thy command,
   Vast as eternity thy love;
   Firm as a rock thy truth must stand,
   When rolling years shall cease to move. Amen.

14. This, this is the day

Brian Howard

Lord has made; let us re-joice
Lord our God; we will re-joice
out the land; the king-dom of God
you who sing, giv-ing thanks and praise

guitar rhythms:

*G6 *A 1.-4. D D.S.

and be glad in it!
and be glad in him!
is at hand!
in ev-'ry - thing!

Final ending
D   C9   G

it!

D

*C9   F Maj7

G6   A

15. There's a river of praise

Capo 2 (C)

Cecilie Hobson

1. There's a riv - er of praise_ with - in_ my heart which is flow - ing full and free, for Je - sus Christ_ came_ down_ from heav'n; he_ died to set_ me free. He_ took a - way my_ fear and shame by the pow'r of his_ great

2. He_ gives me_ joy_ as a gar-ment of praise and_ by his Spi - rit, peace. His ways are ways_ of gen tle - ness; all_ an - xious cares_ can cease. For the love of the Lord is a deep, deep love which_ flows e - ter - nal-

16. Clap your hands

Kevin O'Neill

sing, sing, sing to the Lord;—

for in his life our lives have been re-

stored.

1,2,3.
Final ending

1. O-pen your eyes, it's a brand new day; look and see the stone's been rolled a -
2. See— his hands and— see his side; ris - en from the dead is he who
3. If— the Son has— set us free, then— we— shall be free in -

way! _____
died. _____
deed. _____

O - pen your_ heart and pre -
Run and tell the world that he's
See_ how_ pleas - ant_

pare the way:_____
heard our cry and
it can be for

don't_ be a - fraid to stand and
of - fers his_ life to sat - is -
us_ to_ live in u - ni -

say: _____
fy. _____
ty! _____

Light, rhythmic hand-clapping may be used to good effect:

*G open5

17. Fill your heart with love

(2-part round)

Mike Beck

Wiley Beveridge
Arr. Betty Pulkingham

(1a) Fill your heart with love; _____
(1b) Fill your life with song; _____

(2a) Glo - - - - - - - - - ry _____ in the
(2b) san - na, ho - san - - - - na _____ to the

God _____ is love. _____
God _____ be praised. _____

high - - - - - - - - - - - - - - - est! _____ Ho -
Lord! _____

Last time only

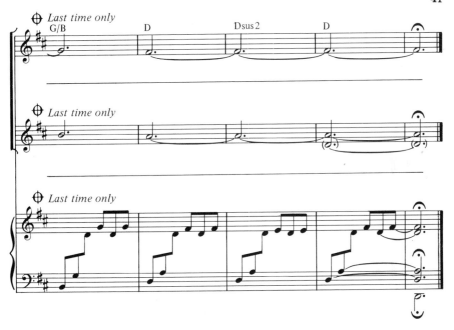

*One suggestion for singing round follows: After all have sung verses 1 and 2 in unison, women only sing verse 1, men joining (on verse 1) as women begin verse 2. Then women repeat verse 1 while men sing verse 2. Finish off with all singing verse 1 again. (You may wish to harmonize the final phrase: see below.)

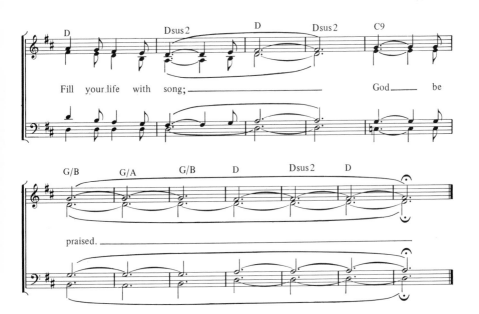

18. Praise, my soul, the King of heaven

Based on Psalm 103
H. F. Lyte

'Lauda Anima'
John Goss
Descant Betty Pulkingham

With breadth

1. Praise, my soul, the King of hea - ven, To his feet thy tri-bute bring;
2. Praise him for his grace and fav - our To our fa-thers in dis - tress;
3. Fa - ther like, he tends and spares us, Well our fee-ble frame he knows;

Ran-somed, healed, re-stored, for - giv - en, Who like me his praise should sing?
Praise him still the same as ev - er, Slow to chide and swift to bless:
In his hands he gen-tly bears us, Res-cues us from all our foes:

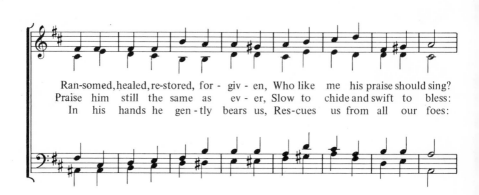

Al - le - lu - ia! Al - le - lu - ia! Praise the ev - er - last-ing King.
Al - le - lu - ia! Al - le - lu - ia! Glo-rious in his faith-ful - ness.
Al - le - lu - ia! Al - le - lu - ia! Wide-ly as his mer - cy flows.

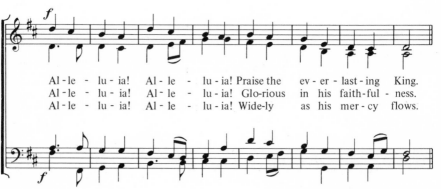

43

19. Tell out, my soul

Adapted from Luke 1:46-55 (Magnificat)
Timothy Dudley-Smith

'Woodlands'
Walter Greatorex

Boldly, not slow

20. In the presence of your people

(The celebration song)

Psalm 22:3, 25

Brent Chambers

This song may be started at a leisurely speed and sung several times with gradual acceleration of tempo. Out of doors or in a large area there is exciting potential for a circle dance.

21. I will rejoice

Capo 2 (D)
Hab. 3:17; Job 13:15

Jan Harrington

slay me, yet I'll re-joice in the Lord al - way. ____

Other verses may be added:

2. I will trust in the Lord alway. *(repeat)*
   Though the fig trees are barren
      and the cattle all die,
   And the crops have failed
      and the fields empty lie;
   And though he slay me,
      even though he slay me,
   Yet I will trust in the Lord alway.

3. I will sing to the Lord alway . . .

4. I will delight in the Lord alway . . .

5. I will hope in the Lord alway . . .

22. Blessing and honour

(4 - part round)

Louise Jolly

With a lilt

Bless-ing and honour and glo - ry and pow'r, be yours for ev-er and ev - er. A-men.

The instrumental obligato below may be used to add brightness.

23. O for a thousand tongues

Charles Wesley

Betty Pulkingham

The glo - ries of my God and King, The tri-umphs
'Tis mu - sic in the sin - ner's ears, 'Tis life and
His blood can make the foul - est clean, His blood a -

The glo-ries of my God and King, The tri-umphs of— his grace!
'Tis mu-sic in the sin - ner's ears, 'Tis life and health and peace.
His blood can make the foul - est clean, His blood a - vailed for me.

of— his grace!
health and peace.
vailed for me.

2. Je - sus, the name that
3. He breaks the pow'r of
4. He speaks, and list-'ning

Fine

4. He speaks; and, list'ning to his voice,
   New life the dead receive,
   The mournful broken hearts rejoice,
   The humble poor believe.

5. Hear him, ye deaf; his praise, ye dumb,
   Your loosened tongues employ;
   Ye blind, behold your Saviour come;
   And leap, ye lame, for joy!

6. My gracious Master and my God,
   Assist me to proclaim
   And spread through all the earth abroad
   The honours of thy name.

24. Hallelujah.... our God reigns

Rev. 19:6,7

Dale Garratt
Arr. Mimi Farra

SECTION 2

SONGS OF WORSHIP

25. Jesus, your blood

Rebecca MacVean
Arr. Betty Pulkingham

Gentle, slow and sustained

May be sung as a 2 - part round

26. Jesus my Saviour

Robert Stoodley

Je-sus my Sav-iour, oh, how I love you, for you have filled me with your new life. All your heav'n-ly glo-ry you count-ed as noth-ing, and bore the pain of death to make us free. There-fore with all my heart I'll glad-ly sing your praise, and do so all my days to bless your ho-ly name. For God has ex-alt-ed you, seat-ed at the Fa-ther's side.

You shall be— glo - ri-fied, Je - sus,—our King!   Je - sus,—our King!

27. Jesus

Wiley Beveridge
Arr. Betty Pulkingham

Soft and tranquil, not fast

1. Je - sus,_____   Je - sus,_____   Je - -
2. Spi - rit, _____   sweet Spi - rit, _____   fill
3. Fa - ther,_____   oh, Fa - ther,_____   take

- - - - sus.____
my____ heart.____
my____ heart.____

This simple worship song lends itself to vocal harmonies (see chords in piano part).

28. When I survey the wondrous cross

Isaac Watts

'Rockingham'
Arr. Edward Miller
Descant Betty Pulkingham

With deep feeling

Descant

4. Were the___ whole realm___ of___ na - ture___ mine,___ That

1. When I___ sur - vey the won - drous cross Where the young
2. For - bid___ it, Lord, that I should boast, Save in the
3. See, from___ his head, his hands, his feet, Sor - row and

were___ an off - 'ring small; Love so a -

Prince of Glo - ry died,___ My rich - est gain I
cross of Christ, my God:___ All the vain things that
love flow min - gled down!___ Did e'er such love and

maz - ing,___ so di - vine, De - mands my soul,___ my life,___ my all.

count but loss, And pour con - tempt on all___ my pride.
charm me most, I sac - ri - fice them to ___ his blood.
sor - row meet, Or thorns com - pose so rich___ a crown?

4. Were the whole realm of nature mine,
   That were an off'ring far too small;
   Love so amazing, so divine,
   Demands my soul, my life, my all.

29. Worthy the Lamb

(3 - part round)

Richard Gillard

Sustained and slow

Wor - thy the Lamb that was slain for us.

Wor - thy, wor - thy___ the Lamb.___

Blessed the Lamb . . .
Holy the Lamb . . .
Mighty the Lamb . . .
Jesus, the Lamb . . .

30. All the riches of his grace

(two-part song)

Jan Harrington

An effective choral arrangement of this song can be achieved quite simply using Theme 1 (All the riches), Theme 2 (Oh, the blood):
1. Trebles sing Theme 1.
2. Trebles repeat Theme 1 while men sing Theme 2 on neutral syllable (e.g., noo, noo, noo).
3. All sing Theme 2 in its hymn form (3 stanzas).
4. Men sing Theme 1, trebles sing Theme 2 on neutral syllable.
5. Men repeat Theme 1 while trebles sing Theme 2 with words.

31. Jesus, you're a wonder

Capo 1 (E)

Anon.
Arr. Betty Pulkingham

With a gentle rocking rhythm

Other verses may be added:

Jesus, you're the healer; (3x)
You're the healer of my soul. (Singing:)

Refrain

Glory, hallelujah! (3x)
You're the healer of my soul.

Jesus, you're the sunshine . . . lover . . . Saviour, *etc.*

32. Bless the holy name of Jesus

Edith McNeill
Arr. George Mims

day the same._____ } Bless the ho-ly name of
alt your name._____ }

Je - sus, Je - sus, glo - ry to____ his name!

33. Jesus is Lord, alleluia

(2-part round)

Fairly slow, flowing

Philip Moore

Je-sus is Lord, Je-sus is Lord, al - le - lu - ia. Je-sus is

Lord, Je-sus is Lord, al - le - lu - ia. Al - le - lu - ia, al -

le - lu - ia,____ al - le - lu - ia, al - le - lu - ia.

34. Jesus, name above all names

Capo 3 (D)
Patricia Cain

Nada Hearn
Arr. Betty Pulkingham

Sustained and gentle

Je - sus, name a - bove all names, beau- ti - ful Sav - iour, glo- ri -ous Lord, _____ Em- man - u - el —— God is with us, bless - ed Re- deem - er, _____ liv - ing Word. _____

* In bars 1, 2, 5 and 6 the following alternative harmonies may be used:
F(D)   F Maj7 (D Maj7)   F6 (D6)   F Maj7 (D Maj7)

35. His name is wonderful

Audrey Mieir
Arr. Betty Pulkingham

His name is won-der-ful, his name is won-der-ful,
He is the might-y King, mas-ter of ev-'ry-thing.

his name is won-der-ful,
His name is won-der-ful, | Je-sus, my Lord.

Je-sus, my

Lord. He's the great shep-herd, the rock of all a-ges,

al-might-y God is he! Bow down be-fore him,

love and a-dore him; his name is won-der-ful, Je-sus, my Lord.

36. Alleluia, he is coming

Capo 2 (C)

Martha Butler
Arr. Mimi Farra

Full and broad

1. I looked up and I saw my Lord a-com-ing,____
2. I looked up and I saw my Lord a-weep-ing,____
3. I looked up and I saw my Lord a-dy-ing,____

I looked up and I saw my Lord a-com-ing down the
I looked up and I saw my Lord a-weep-ing for my
I looked up and I saw my Lord a-dy-ing on the

road.____
sins.____
cross.____

Refrain

Al - le - lu - ia, he is com-ing,____

4. I looked up and I saw my Lord a-rising,
   I looked up and I saw my Lord a-rising from the grave.

37. There's a quiet understanding

Tedd Smith

Gently, with warmth

There's a qui - et un - der-stand - ing when we're gath-ered
There's a love we feel in Je - sus, there's a man - na

in the Spi - rit, it's a prom-ise that he gives us
that he feeds us,

1. when we gath-er in his name.
2. when we gath - er in his

name. And we know when we're to - geth - er,
Thank you, thank you, thank you, Je - sus,

shar - ing love and   un - der-stand - ing,   that our broth-ers
for the way you   love and feed us,   for the man - y

and our sis - ters   feel the one-ness that he brings.
ways you lead us;

thank you, thank you, Lord.   Thank you, thank you, Lord.

38. Jesus came

Jan Harrington

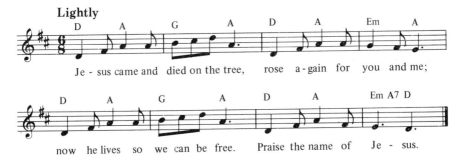

Lightly

Je - sus came and died on the tree,   rose a - gain for you and me;

now he lives so we can be free.   Praise the name of Je - sus.

39. Litany

Rev. Carey Landry
Arr. Betty Pulkingham

With movement, freely

O Lord, our God, we lift up our hearts to you.
O Lord, our God, your peo-ple re-joice in you.

1. God of the liv - ing, God of all peo - ple,
2. Christ Je - sus cru - ci - fied,— wound-ed for man - kind,
3. Great Ho - ly Spi - rit, bright fire of God,—

Fa - ther of__ life,
you gave your__ life for us,— } we lift up our hearts to you.
come, burn in our hearts, O Lord,—

Additional verses may be improvised, e.g. 'River of mercy, oh, sea of peace, ocean of loveliness, we lift up our hearts to you.'

SECTION 3

SONGS OF HOPE, VISION, WHOLENESS

40. I will arise and go to Jesus

Joseph Hart

'Arise'
American folk melody

With deep feeling

1. Come, ye___ sin - ners,___ poor and need - y,
Refrain: *I will a - rise and___ go to Je - sus,*
2. Come, ye___ thirst - y, ___ come, and wel - come,
3. Come, ye___ wea - ry, ___ heav - y la - den,

Weak and___ wound - ed, ___ sick and sore; Je - sus rea - dy
He will em-brace me___ in his arms; In the arms___ of
God's free___ boun - ty___ glo - ri - fy; True be - lief___ and
Lost and___ ru - ined___ by the fall; If you tar - ry

stands to save___ you, Full of pi - ty, love, and pow'r. *(Refrain)*
my dear Sav - iour, Oh, there are___ ten___ thou-sand charms.
true re - pent - ance, Ev - 'ry grace___ that___ brings you nigh. *(Refrain)*
till you're bet - ter, You will nev - er___ come at all. *(Refrain)*

41. Peace, perfect peace

Edward Henry Bickersteth

'Song 46'
Orlando Gibbons
Descant Betty Pulkingham

Quietly

1. Peace, per - fect peace, in this dark world of sin? The blood of Je - sus whis - pers peace with - in.
2. Peace, per - fect peace, by throng - ing du - ties pressed? To do the will of Je - sus, this is rest.
3. Peace, per - fect peace, with sor - rows surg - ing round? On Je - sus' bo - som naught but calm is found.

4. Peace, perfect peace, with loved ones far away?
   In Jesus' keeping we are safe, and they.

5. Peace, perfect peace, our future all unknown?
   Jesus we know, and he is on the throne.

6. Peace, perfect peace, death shadowing us and ours?
   Jesus has vanquished death and all its powers.

7. It is enough: earth's struggles soon shall cease,
   And Jesus call us to heav'n's perfect peace.

Optional reharmonization and descant

7. It is e - nough, — e - nough: earth's strug - gles

Unison

(powers) 7. It is e - nough: earth's strug- gles soon shall

cease, And Je - sus call us to heav'n's per - fect peace.

cease, And Je - sus call us to heav'n's per - fect peace.

42. The fear of the Lord
(2 - part round)

Proverbs 9:10

Shirley Lewis Brown

Smoothly, not fast

The fear of the Lord is the be - gin - ning of wis- dom, and the

know - ledge of the ho - ly is un - der - stand - ing.

43. Trust in the Lord

Proverbs 3:5, 6, 23, 24; 2:3-5

Mimi Farra

Quietly, sustained

Refrain

Trust in the Lord with all thine heart, lean not un-to thine own un-der-stand - - - ing; in all thy ways ac-know-ledge him, and he shall dir-ect___ thy paths._____

44. The bridegroom's song

With a martial air

John Mc Neil
Arr. Shirley Lewis Brown

Sound on the trum-pet, call to the peo - ple, sing your new
Break out the ban -ners, join in the dan - cing, no time for

song. Our bride-groom's com - ing, it won't be
gloom. Pre - pare the ban - quet, he's com - ing

long.
soon.

1. If you're _____
2. Go out _____

_____ one of God's peo - ple, _____ re - joice _____
_____ with tears and weep - ing _____ to bring _____

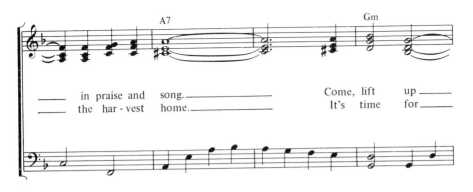

in praise and song.___ Come, lift up ___
the har-vest home.___ It's time for___

your hearts be-fore him___ and give your voic - es ___
the joy of reap-ing;___ in joy the sheaves now___

in praise and song. ___
are com-ing home. ___

This song may be started at a slow but rhythmic pace, then accelerated with each repetition until desired degree of speed and excitement are generated. (Needless to say, it is important to stop while people are still enjoying it!)

45. Fill my cup, Lord

Richard Blanchard
Arr. Betty Pulkingham

Slowly, with expression

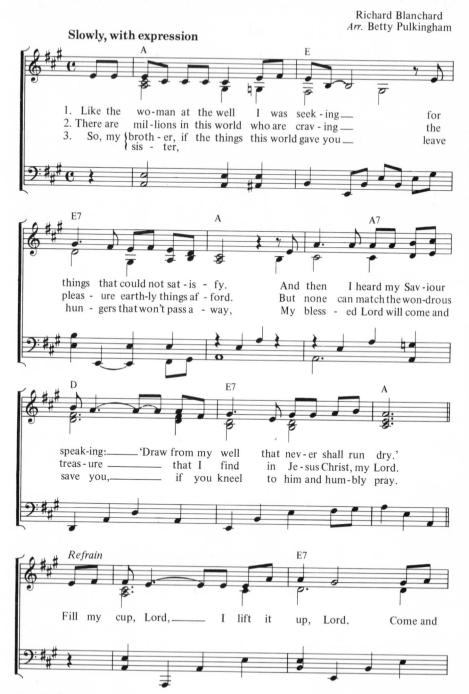

1. Like the wo-man at the well I was seek-ing___ for things that could not sat-is-fy. And then I heard my Sav-iour speak-ing:___ 'Draw from my well that nev-er shall run dry.'

2. There are mil-lions in this world who are crav-ing___ the pleas-ure earth-ly things af-ford. But none can match the won-drous treas-ure ___ that I find in Je-sus Christ, my Lord.

3. So, my {broth-er, sis-ter,} if the things this world gave you___ leave hun-gers that won't pass a-way, My bless-ed Lord will come and save you,___ if you kneel to him and hum-bly pray.

Refrain

Fill my cup, Lord,___ I lift it up, Lord, Come and

quench this thirst-ing of my soul. Bread of heav-en, feed me till I

want no more. Fill my cup, fill it up and make me whole.

46. They that wait upon the Lord

Isaiah 40:31

Composer unknown

At a leisurely pace

They that wait — up-on the Lord shall re - new _____ their _____

strength. They shall mount up with wings as the

ea - gle. _____ They shall run _____ and not be

wear - y, they shall walk _____ and not _____ faint. Teach me,

Lord, teach me, Lord, _____ to wait. _____

47. Come, Lord Jesus

Capo 2 (G)

Diane Davis Andrew

48. Awake, awake to love and work

G. Studdert-Kennedy

'Morning Song'
American folk melody
Arr. George Mims

Brightly, with movement

1. A - wake, a - wake to love and work! The lark is in the sky, The fields are wet with dia - mond dew, The worlds a - wake to cry Their bless - ings on the Lord of life, As he goes meek - ly by.
2. Come, let thy voice be one with theirs, Shout with their shout of praise; See how the gi - ant sun soars up, Great lord of years and days! So let the love of Je - sus come And set thy soul a blaze,
3. To give, and give, and give a - gain What God hath giv - en thee; To spend thy - self nor count the cost; To serve right glo - rious - ly The God who gave all worlds that are, And all that are to be.

49. Fear not, for I have redeemed you

Based on Isaiah 43

Jodi Page Clark
Arr. Pat Allen

With breadth, not too slow

Fear not, for I have re - deemed you;

I have called you by name.

1. When you pass through the wa-ters I will __ be with you; _____ And through
2. Be-cause you are pre-cious and I __ love __ you, _____
3. You are my wit-ness-es; I have cho-sen you _____
4. It's time now to lay a-side the __ for-mer things; __
5. The riv-ers that flow __ in the __ des-ert _____ Give __

50. Tell my people

Anon.
Verses and descant Jan Harrington

With warmth

Refrain

Tell my peo-ple I love them,

tell my peo-ple I care.

When they feel far a - way from me,

tell my peo-ple I am there.

Em

1. Tell my peo - ple I came and died _____
2. Tell my peo - ple where - e'er they go _____

A7   D

_____ to give them lib - er - ty, _____ and to a -
_____ my com-fort they can know. _____ My peace and

Em   A7   D   *D.C.*

bide in me _____ is to be real - ly free.
joy and love _____ I free - ly will be - stow.

Optional descant for refrain

Tell my peo - ple that I love them, tell my peo - ple I

care. When they feel far a - way from me tell them I am there.

51. Pure light

Capo 3 (A)

Mimi Farra

With quiet simplicity

1. Pure light of the Son of God, shine on my path that I may
2. Pure mind of the Son of God, come and think your thoughts in
3. Pure love of the Son of God, fill my heart that I may
4. Spirit of the Son of God, live in me that I may
5. Jesus Christ, who sets us free, calls to you and calls to

see the way where-in you have called me to go.
me. (7) One thought on - ly would I know:
show the love you have for all man-kind,
do the will of God and be set free to
me to fol-low him to the Fa-ther's throne,

Shine on my path that I may fol-low you.
Son of God, you love me so.
love that is e-ter-nal life.
live the life of Je-sus Christ.
there to dwell for e-ter-ni-ty.

52. Lord, give us your Spirit

Sandy Hardyman

Slow and sustained

Refrain

Lord, give us your Spi-rit, __ your Spi-rit __ that is love. __

Lord, fill us with your life, __ free-ly giv-en __ for the world. __

1. Where __ child-ren cry __ let us wipe their tears __ a - way, __ and
2. Where __ there is pain __ let us be your heal - ing hands, __ and
3. Where __ peo-ple hate __ let us dwell a-mong them with love, __ and

where __ child-ren fall __ let us raise them to their feet.
where __ there is grief __ let us com - fort with your love.
where __ peo-ple fight __ let us bind their deep-est wounds.

53. 'Lu-ia, 'lu-ia

Max Dyer

With rhythmic drive

Additional verses may be added, for example:

Packed my bags today, 'lu-ia, 'lu-ia,
Goin' far away, 'lu-ia, 'lu-ia,
Whether I go or stay, 'lu-ia, 'lu-ia,
I will sing to you.

Pillar of cloud by day, 'lu-ia, 'lu-ia,
Pillar of fire by night, 'lu-ia, 'lu-ia,
By the Spirit we are led, 'lu-ia, 'lu-ia,
We will sing to you.

This song originated at a time when the Community of Celebration, Berkshire, England, dispersed in three directions to expand its life and ministry. Verses may be adapted or added to celebrate times of change and challenge in your situation.

54. There's a new song in the land

John Smith
Arr. Mimi Farra

SECTION 4

SONGS OF THE KINGDOM

55. Jesus is our King

Capo 4 (C)
Sherrell Prebble and Howard Clark

'Post Green'
Sherrell Prebble

With joyful dignity

Al - le - lu - ia! Al - le - lu - ia! O - pen - ing our

hearts to him, Sing - ing al - le - lu - ia!

Al - le - lu - ia! Je - sus is our King!

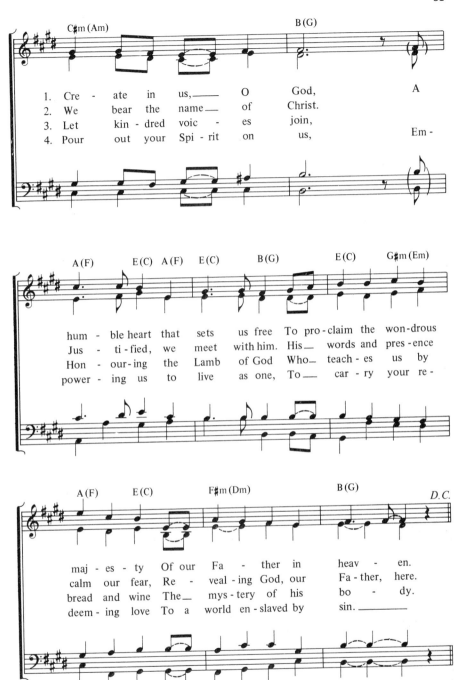

*Guitar chords are designed to be used only when the entire song is sung in unison.

56. The fishermen

William Alexander Percy

'Fisherfolk'
Betty Pulkingham

Unison with optional alto part
Expressive and lyrical

1. They cast their nets___ in Gal - i - lee___ Just
2. Con - tent - ed, peace - ful fish - er - men,___ Be -
3. Young John who trimm'd the flap - ping sail, ___ Home-
4. The peace of God,___ it is no peace,___ But

off___ the hills of brown; ___ Such hap - py,
fore___ they ev - er knew___ The peace of
- less, in Pat - mos died.___ Pe - ter, who
strife___ clos'd in the sod. ___ Yet, broth - ers,

57. People of God

(Pueblo de Dios)

Anon.
Tr. Susan Abbott

Basque melody

Rich and warm

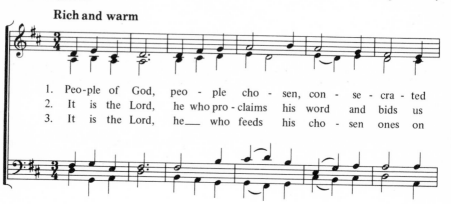

1. Peo-ple of God, peo - ple cho - sen, con - se - cra - ted
2. It is the Lord, he who pro - claims his word and bids us
3. It is the Lord, he__ who feeds his cho - sen ones on

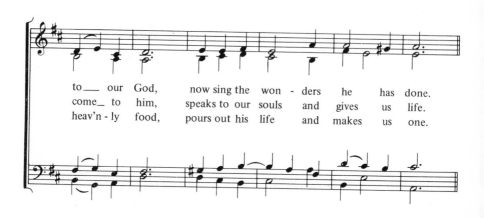

to__ our God, now sing the won - ders he has done.
come_ to him, speaks to our souls and gives us life.
heav'n - ly food, pours out his life and makes us one.

Refrain

We glo - ri - fy our God_ on high, cel - e - brate his

1. Pueblo de Dios, pueblo elegido y consagrado
   Para cantar las maravillas del Señor:

Refrain

    ¡Glorifiquemos a nuestro Dios,
    Y celebremos su gran amor,
    Aleluya, aleluya!

2. Es el Señor quien nos anuncia su palabra,
   Es el Señor quien nos invita a la oración:

3. Es el Señor quien alimenta nuestra vida,
   Es el Señor quien se nos da en comunión:

58. Hiney mah tov

Israeli round

Brightly, rhythmically

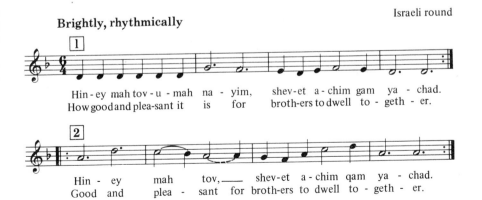

59. Gift of finest wheat

Omer Westendorf

Robert E. Kreutz

With simple lyricism

Refrain

You sat-is-fy the hun-gry heart ___ With gift of fin-est wheat; Come give to us, O ___ sav-ing Lord, The bread of life to eat. ___

Fine

1. As when the shep - herd calls his sheep, They
2. With joy - ful lips we sing to you Our
3. Is not the cup we bless and share The
4. The mys-t'ry of your pres - ence, Lord, No
5. You give your-self to us, O Lord; Then

know   and heed his   voice;
praise   and grat - i - tude,
blood   of Christ out - poured?
mor -   tal tongue can tell:
self -   less let   us   be,

So   when you call   your
That you should count us
Do   not one cup,   one
Whom all   the world can -
To   serve each oth - er

D.C.

fam - 'ly, Lord, We   fol - low and re - joice.
wor - thy, Lord, To   share   this heav'n-ly food.
loaf, de - clare Our one - ness in the   Lord?
not con - tain   Comes in   our hearts to dwell.
in   your name   In   truth   and char - i - ty.

60. My sheep hear my voice
(6 - part round)

Donna Wilson

Brightly

My sheep hear my voice, I know them, I know them. My sheep hear my voice, they fol - low me. I give life e - ter-nal and they shall not per-ish, I give life e - ter-nal and they shall not per-ish; and none shall pluck them from my hand, and none shall pluck them from my hand.

61. Praise God for the body

Capo 3 (Em)

Anne Ortlund
Arr. Betty Pulkingham

*Christian

*Christians

62. Good evening, Father

Murray Davis
Arr. Betty Pulkingham

Gently, with a bounce

Good eve - ning, Fa - ther, we de - light to do your will;
(morn - ing)

good eve - ning, Fa - ther, as we seek our hearts to fill with the
(morn - ing)

praise of your glo - ry and the light of your word. With each

'good eve - ning, Fa - ther' we'll love you a little bit more!
(morn - ing)

63. The Lord's prayer

(from 'El Shaddai' setting)

Betty Pulkingham

Hand movements for congregation (standing or seated)

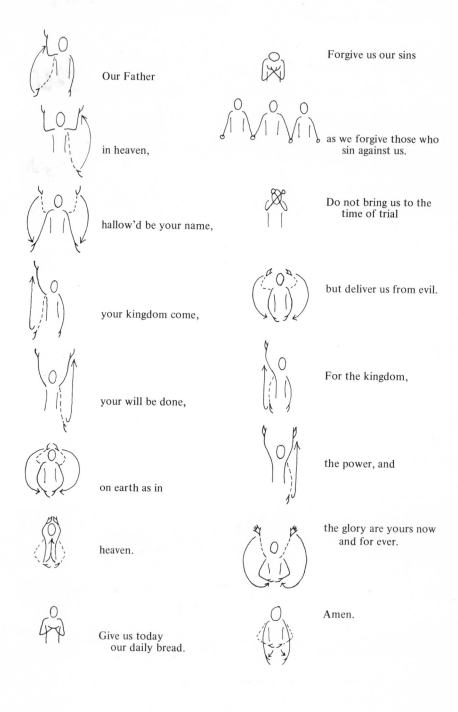

Our Father

in heaven,

hallow'd be your name,

your kingdom come,

your will be done,

on earth as in

heaven.

Give us today
our daily bread.

Forgive us our sins

as we forgive those who
sin against us.

Do not bring us to the
time of trial

but deliver us from evil.

For the kingdom,

the power, and

the glory are yours now
and for ever.

Amen.

64. How much greater

Based on Hebrews 9:14

Phillip Bailey
Arr. Betty Pulkingham

Simply, with warmth

1. How much great-er is the pow'r of the blood of Christ our Lord! Of-fer-ing him-self, he be-came the liv-ing Word; Christ the Lord, his life out-pour-ing.
2. But now Christ has come to us, an e-ter-nal sac-ri-fice. Cleans-ing us from sin, he gives us new life with-in; Christ the Lord, his love out-pour-ing.
3. Fa-ther, we give thanks to you for your Son who makes us one. By his love so free we be-come your fam-i-ly; Christ the Lord, him-self out-pour-ing.

Rit.

This charming song came about as a group of Christians in Australia studied the Epistle to the Hebrews. We suggest that you read Chapter 9, especially verse 13, before singing it.

65. We are coming, Lord

Kathy Wood
Arr. Mimi Farra

Slowly
Refrain

We are com-ing, Lord, _____ to your

ta - ble. _____ We are com - ing _____

_____ to eat and drink to re-mem - ber you. _____

1. We come as one bo - dy, u - ni - ted in your
2. We come, though un - wor-thy, to gath - er up the
3. We come___ re - joic-ing, with hearts for ev - er

spi - rit,___ broth - ers,___ sis - ters, young and old, to
crumbs; yet healed, re -stored, for - giv - en, through
prais - ing, and lips___ that are sing - ing of

cel - e - brate your life___ for___ us.___
Je - sus, who died___ for___ us.___
Je - sus, who lives___ in___ us.___

66. Children at your feet

Bill Pulkingham (vs. 1 and 2)
Martha Barker (v. 3)

Bill Pulkingham

tell my peo-ple__ that I__ care; _____
all__ of__ their wealth and__ pain; _____
as they so - journ_ through this__ land. _____

for my peace is for them to live__ in, _____
for my Spirit is not one of greed, _____
I have gone this way be - fore__ them, _____

for my peace is for them__ to share. _____
for my Spirit is not one__ of shame. _____
now I guide them by_____ my hand. _____

dim. —————— *pp*

will,___ just rea-dy to do_ your will,___ just rea-dy to do_your will.__

67. Be like your Father

Beverlee Paine

But I say unto you, love your en-e-mies and pray for those who hurt you. Give to those who ask, don't turn a-way. And be like your Fa-ther in hea-ven a-bove who caus-es his sun to shine on e-vil and good, and sends down his rain

to quench all our thirst. In him we live and
move and have our be - ing. _____

1. If you for -
2. When you

give each oth - er, so will God for - give ___ you. _____
see the hun - gry, feed them from your ta - ble. _____

For the

Do not judge lest you be judg'd your - selves. _____
poor and wea - ry, be their wat - 'ring place. _____

And
And

68. Broken for me

Colin and Janet Lunt
Arr. Mimi Farra

Sustained

Refrain

Bro-ken for me,_____ bro-ken for you; the bo-dy of

Last time

Je - sus _____ bro-ken for you.

1. He of-fered his bo - dy,_____ he poured out his
2. Come to my ta - ble _____ and with me
3. This is my bo - dy _____ giv - en for
4. This is my blood _____ I shed for

69. Harvest of righteousness

Capo 3 (Em)
Vs. 1-3 based on 2 Cor. 9, Isaiah 16, 17

Bill and Margi Pulkingham

Relaxed, not too fast

1. He___ who sup - plies _____ seed to the sow - er___ and bread for___ food will sup - ply___ and___
2. Of - fer - ing your ser - vice sup - plies the___ wants___ of the saints___ and pleas - es our___ God.___
3. Glo - ri - fy___ God by___ your o - be - di - ence, ac - know - ledge the gos - pel of___ Christ.___ The ef -
(4.) claim___ with your heart _____ great thanks - giv - ing for the gift of___ Je - sus our___ Lord.___ Be -

70. The servant song

Richard Gillard
Arr. Betty Pulkingham

Capo 1 (D)

With warmth, moving along

1. and 6 †Broth-er, let me be your ser–vant, let me be as Christ to you;
2. We are pil-grims on a jour-ney, we are†broth-ers on the road;
3. I will hold the Christ-light for you in the night-time of your fear;

pray that I may have the grace to let you be my ser - vant, too.
we are here to help each oth-er walk the mile and bear___ the load.
I will hold my hand out to you, speak the peace you long___ to hear.

4. I will weep when you are weeping;
   When you laugh I'll laugh with you.
   I will share your joy and sorrow
   'Til we've seen this journey through.

5. When we sing to God in heaven
   We shall find such harmony,
   Born of all we've known together
   Of Christ's love and agony.

*Guitar chords and vocal harmonies are not designed to be used together.
† or 'Sister', 'sisters'

71. The celebration song

Jonathan Asprey
and Tim Whipple

Brisk and well-accented

1. For our life to-geth-er, we cel-e-brate.__ Life that lasts for ev-er, we cel-e-brate.__
3. For his bo-dy, bro-ken, we cel-e-brate.__ For the word he's spo-ken, we cel-e-brate.__

vs. 3 † by his grace

Am   D7   † by his grace

For the joy and for the sor - row, yes - ter- day, to -day,
For the feast - ing at his ta - ble, † by his grace

D7   G

___ to-mor - row, we cel - e - brate.___
we are a - ble to cel - e - brate.___

C   G

2. For your
4. For the

C

great cre-a - tion, we cel - e - brate.___
Lord a - bove, ___ we cel - e - brate.___

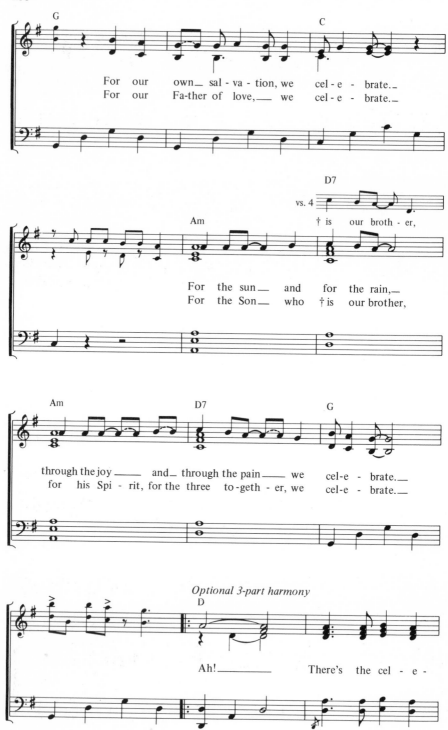

For our own__ sal - va - tion, we cel - e - brate.__
For our Fa-ther of love,__ we cel - e - brate.__

vs. 4
† is our broth - er,

For the sun__ and for the rain,__
For the Son__ who † is our brother,

through the joy ____ and__ through the pain ____ we cel-e - brate.__
for his Spi - rit, for the three to-geth - er, we cel-e - brate.__

Optional 3-part harmony

Ah!_____ There's the cel - e -

72. Jerusalem is fair

Willard F. Jabusch

'Church of the Redeemer'
Betty Pulkingham

With breadth and dignity

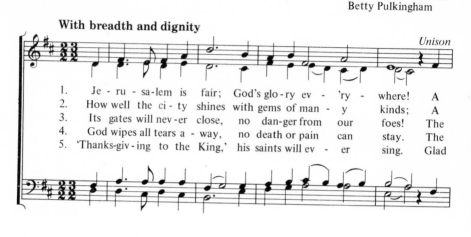

1. Je - ru - sa - lem is fair; God's glo - ry ev - 'ry - where! A
2. How well the ci - ty shines with gems of man - y kinds; A
3. Its gates will nev - er close, no dan - ger from our foes! The
4. God wipes all tears a - way, no death or pain can stay. The
5. 'Thanks - giv - ing to the King,' his saints will ev - er sing. Glad

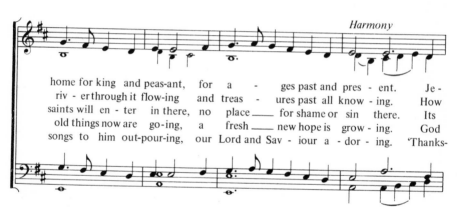

home for king and peas - ant, for a - ges past and pres - ent. Je -
riv - er through it flow - ing and treas - ures past all know - ing. How
saints will en - ter in there, no place for shame or sin there. Its
old things now are go - ing, a fresh new hope is grow - ing. God
songs to him out - pour - ing, our Lord and Sav - iour a - dor - ing. 'Thanks-

ru - sa - lem is fair; God's glo - ry ev - 'ry - where!
well the ci - ty shines with gems of man - y kinds.
gates will nev - er close, no dan - ger from our foes!
wipes all tears a - way, no death or pain can stay.
giv - ing to the King,' his saints will ev - er sing.

SECTION 5

SONGS OF FAITH AND VICTORY

73. He's able

Paul E. Paino
Arr. Betty Pulkingham

Resolutely

He's a - ble, he's a - ble, I know he's a - ble, I know my Lord is a - ble to car - ry me through. He's

1.

2. He heals the bro-ken heart-ed, and sets the cap-tive free, he makes the lame to walk a - gain and he caus-es the blind to see. He's

'He's able' may be sung in sequence with the following song.

74. Whosoever will

Composer unknown
Arr. Betty Pulkingham

Happily

Who - so - ev - er will to the Lord may come;

who - so - ev - er will to the Lord may come; who - so - ev - er will to the

Lord may come, he'll not turn one a - way.

*Refrain

Je - sus, Je - sus, Je - sus, Je - sus heals the

bro - ken heart - ed; Je - sus, Je - sus, Je - sus, Je - sus

heals the bro - ken heart - ed; Je - sus, Je - sus, Je - sus, Je - sus

heals the bro - ken heart - ed, he will set you free.

*Refrain effective when sung antiphonally by treble and male voices.

75. O love, how deep

Latin, 15th cent.
Tr. Benjamin Webb

'Deus Tuorum Militum'
Grenoble Church Melody
Descant Betty Pulkingham

In unison, with stately dignity

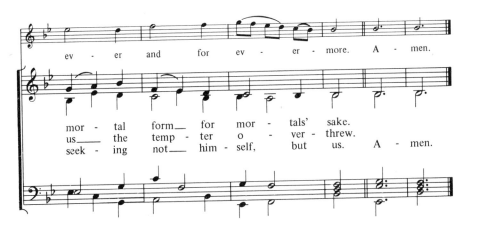

ev - er and for ev - er - more. A - men.

mor - tal form__ for mor - tals' sake.
us__ the temp - ter o - ver - threw.
seek - ing not__ him - self, but us. A - men.

4. For us to wicked men betrayed,
   Scourged, mocked, in purple robe arrayed,
   He bore the shameful cross and death;
   For us gave up his dying breath.

5. For us he rose from death again,
   For us he went on high to reign;
   For us he sent his Spirit here
   To guide, to strengthen, and to cheer.

6. All glory to our Lord and God
   For love so deep, so high, so broad;
   The Trinity whom we adore
   For ever and for evermore. Amen.

76. I will sing of the mercies

Psalm 89:1

J. H. Fillmore
Arr. Betty Pulkingham

77. For you are my God

From Psalm 16

John B. Foley, S.J.
Arr. George Mims
and Betty Pulkingham

Broad and majestic
Refrain

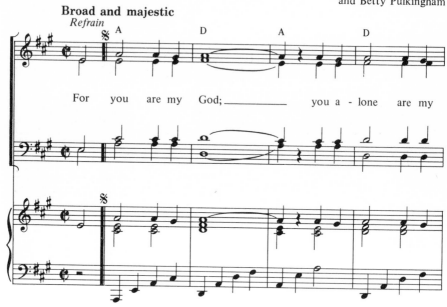

For you are my God; _____ you a - lone are my

joy. _____ De - fend me, O Lord. _____

1. You give mar-vel-ous com-rades to me: the
2. You are my por-tion and cup; it is

faith-ful who dwell in your land. Your
you that I claim for my prize.

133

78. Great is thy faithfulness

Thomas O. Chisholm

'Faithfulness'
William M. Runyan

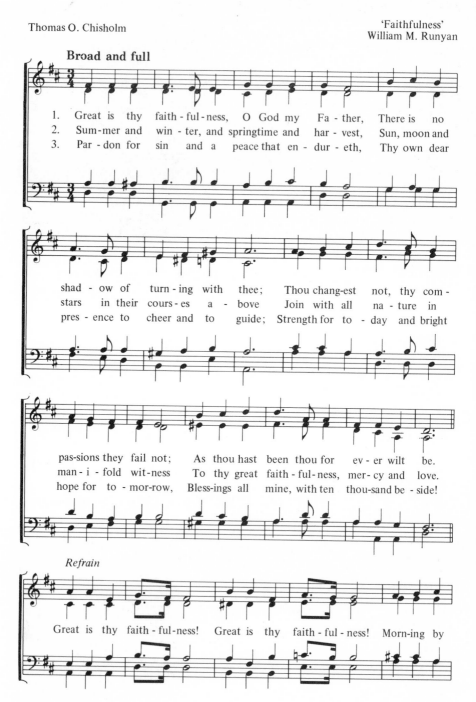

Broad and full

1. Great is thy faith-ful-ness, O God my Fa-ther, There is no
2. Sum-mer and win-ter, and springtime and har-vest, Sun, moon and
3. Par-don for sin and a peace that en-dur-eth, Thy own dear

shad-ow of turn-ing with thee; Thou chang-est not, thy com-
stars in their cours-es a-bove Join with all na-ture in
pres-ence to cheer and to guide; Strength for to-day and bright

pas-sions they fail not; As thou hast been thou for ev-er wilt be.
man-i-fold wit-ness To thy great faith-ful-ness, mer-cy and love.
hope for to-mor-row, Bless-ings all mine, with ten thou-sand be-side!

Refrain

Great is thy faith-ful-ness! Great is thy faith-ful-ness! Morn-ing by

morn-ing new mer-cies I see; All I have need-ed thy

hand hath pro - vid-ed— Great is thy faith-ful-ness, Lord, un - to me!

79. Awake, O sleeper

(4 - part round)

Ephesians 5:14

Louise Jolly

Brightly

A - wake, O sleep - er, rise up from the dead. A - wake, O sleep - er, rise

up from the dead, and Christ will give _____ you light. _____

80. How great thou art!

Stuart K. Hine

'O Store Gud'
Swedish folk melody

Broad and full

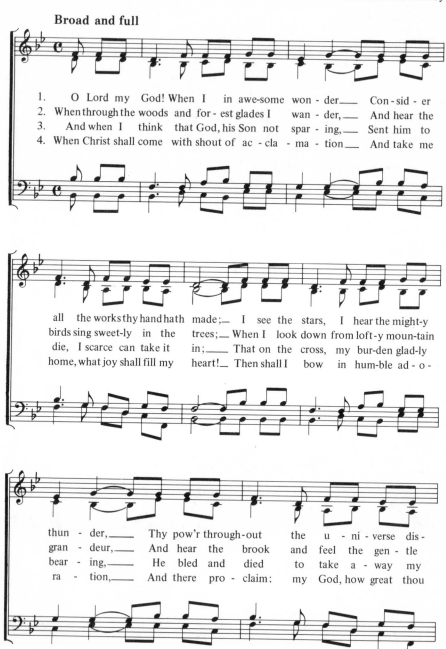

1. O Lord my God! When I in awe-some won - der____ Con-sid - er
2. When through the woods and for - est glades I wan - der, ____ And hear the
3. And when I think that God, his Son not spar - ing, ____ Sent him to
4. When Christ shall come with shout of ac - cla - ma - tion____ And take me

all the works thy hand hath made;__ I see the stars, I hear the might-y
birds sing sweet-ly in the trees;__ When I look down from loft-y moun-tain
die, I scarce can take it in;____ That on the cross, my bur-den glad-ly
home, what joy shall fill my heart!__ Then shall I bow in hum-ble ad - o -

thun - der, ____ Thy pow'r through-out the u - ni - verse dis -
gran - deur, ____ And hear the brook and feel the gen - tle
bear - ing, ____ He bled and died to take a - way my
ra - tion, ____ And there pro - claim: my God, how great thou

played:
breeze: Then sings my soul,   my Sav-iour God, to thee, How great thou art! How
sin:
art!

great thou art!____   Then sings my   soul,   my Sav - iour God,   to

thee, How great thou art!   How great   thou   art!____

Alternative ending

thee,____   How great thou art!____   How great   thou   art!____

81. I know whom I have believed

D. W. Whittle

James Mc Granahan
Arr. Betty Pulkingham

Lyrical

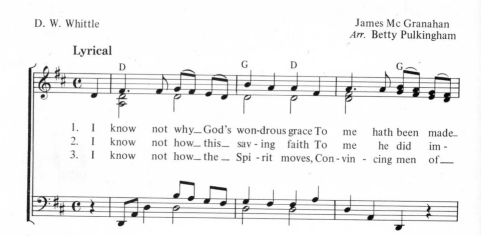

1. I know not why_ God's won-drous grace To me hath been made_
2. I know not how_ this_ sav - ing faith To me he did im -
3. I know not how_ the_ Spi - rit moves, Con - vin - cing men of_

known; Nor why, un - wor - thy_ as I am, He
part; Or how be - liev - ing_ in his word Wrought
sin; Re - veal - ing Je - sus_ through the word, Cre -

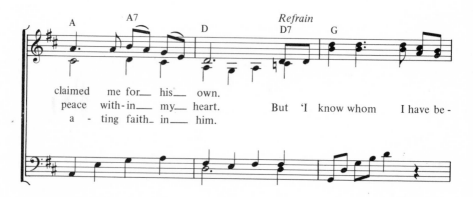

claimed me for_ his_ own.
peace with - in_ my_ heart. But 'I know whom I have be -
a - ting faith_ in_ him.

liev - ed; and am per - suad - ed that he is a - ble to

keep that which I've com-mit - ed un-to him a-gainst that day'.——

4. I know not what of good or ill
   May be reserved for me—
   Of weary ways or golden days
   Before his face I see.

5. I know not when my Lord may come;
   I know not how, nor where;
   If I shall pass the vale of death,
   Or 'meet him in the air.'

82. On Christ the solid rock

Edward Mote

'Solid Rock'
William B. Bradbury

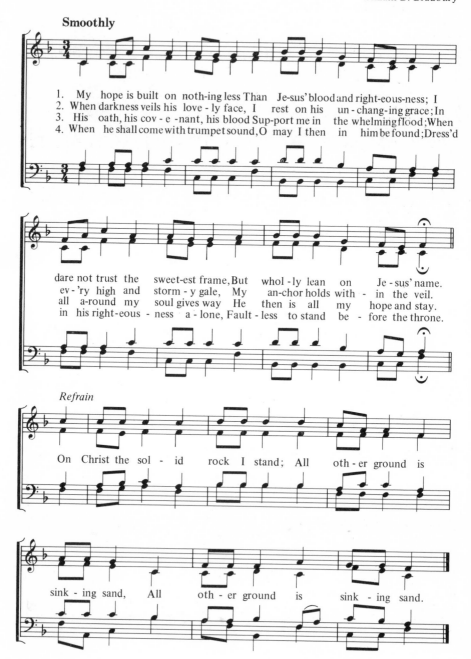

Smoothly

1. My hope is built on noth-ing less Than Je-sus' blood and right-eous-ness; I
2. When darkness veils his love - ly face, I rest on his un - chang-ing grace; In
3. His oath, his cov - e -nant, his blood Sup-port me in the whelming flood; When
4. When he shall come with trumpet sound, O may I then in him be found; Dress'd

dare not trust the sweet-est frame, But whol -ly lean on Je - sus' name.
ev -'ry high and storm - y gale, My an-chor holds with - in the veil.
all a-round my soul gives way He then is all my hope and stay.
in his right-eous - ness a - lone, Fault - less to stand be - fore the throne.

Refrain

On Christ the sol - id rock I stand; All oth - er ground is

sink - ing sand, All oth - er ground is sink - ing sand.

83. Living Lord

Patrick Appleford

Freely, with movement

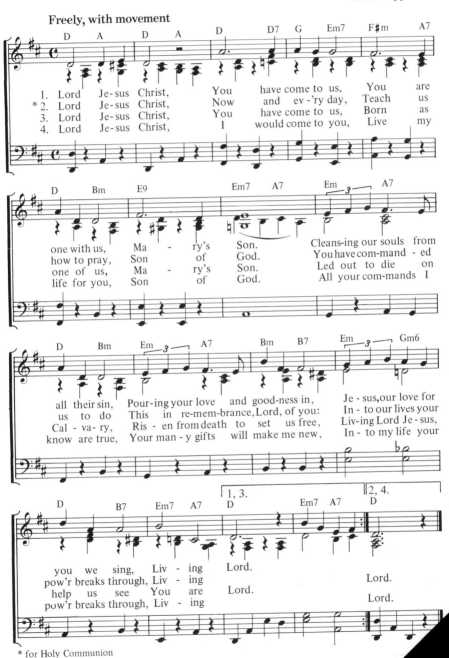

1. Lord Jesus Christ, You have come to us, You are one with us, Mary's Son. Cleansing our souls from all their sin, Pouring your love and goodness in, Jesus, our love for you we sing, Living Lord.

*2. Lord Jesus Christ, Now and ev'ry day, Teach us how to pray, Son of God. You have commanded us to do This in remembrance, Lord, of you: Into our lives your pow'r breaks through, Living Lord.

3. Lord Jesus Christ, You have come to us, Born as one of us, Mary's Son. Led out to die on Calvary, Risen from death to set us free, Living Lord Jesus, help us see You are Lord.

4. Lord Jesus Christ, I would come to you, Live my life for you, Son of God. All your commands I know are true, Your many gifts will make me new, Into my life your pow'r breaks through, Living Lord.

* for Holy Communion

84. Ballad of the dance

Sandy Hardyman

Liltingly

Refrain Sing hal - le - lu - jah to the Fa - ther, _____ sing
5. 'Come _____ to me as lit - tle child - ren; _____

hal - le - lu - jah to his on - ly Son, _____ sing
come, _____ and put your hand in mine. _____

prais - es to the Ho - ly Spi - rit; _____
Come, and I will set your feet a - dan - cing; _____

_____ in One. _____ 1. In _____
_____ goes _____ on.' _____ (D.C.) 2. The dis-
3. A _____

20th Century Hymn

144

85. When led by the Spirit

All I do is be - lieve, _____

All I do, all I do is be -

lieve. _____

ritard. *(last time)*

2. When led by the Spirit, a blind man sees,
   A deaf man hears, a crippled man walks!
   If you're led by the Spirit, you will see,
   You will hear, you will walk!
   God gave you his Son;
   He is the only one.
   Jesus came and he died.
   But there's one thing, my friend,
   That in the very end
   Jesus rose from the dead.
   All you do is believe,
   All you do, all you do is believe.

3. Lord, I was blind but now I see,
   Now I hear, now I walk!
   Lord, we were blind but now we see,
   Now we hear, now we walk!
   God gave us his Son;
   He is the only one.
   Jesus came and he died.
   But there's one thing, my friend,
   That in the very end
   Jesus rose from the dead.
   My Lord, my God, we believe.
   My Lord, my God, my Lord, my God, we believe.

SECTION 6

SONGS OF OUTREACH

86. Everybody song

Robert Stoodley

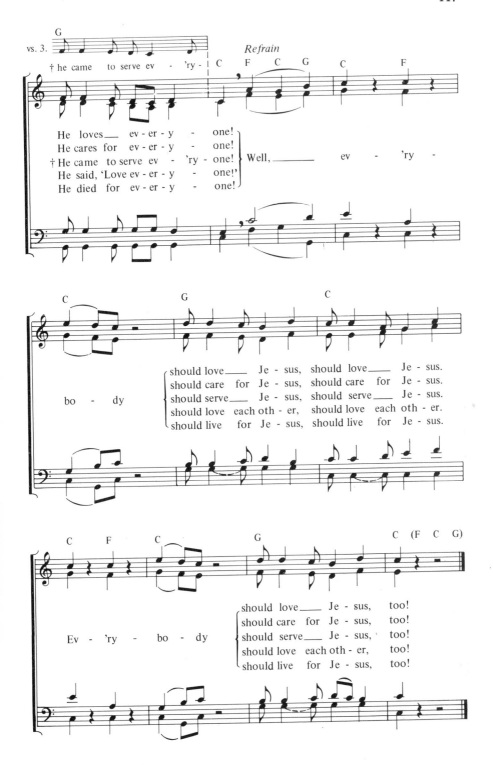

87. Jesus shall reign

Isaac Watts

'Duke Street'
John Hatton
Descant Betty Pulkingham

With breadth *Descant*

5. Let ev-'ry crea-ture rise ____ and ____ bring Pe-cu-liar ____ hon-ours to ____ our ____ King; An-gels de-scend ____ with songs ____ a - gain, And

1. Je - sus shall reign wher - e'er the ____ sun
2. To him shall end - less ____ prayer be ____ made,
3. Peo - ple and realms of ____ ev - 'ry ____ tongue

Doth his suc - ces - sive jour - neys run;
And prais - es throng to crown his head;
Dwell on his love with sweet - est song;

His king-dom stretch ____ from ____ shore ____ to ____ shore,
His name like sweet ____ per - fume ____ shall ____ rise
And in - fant voic - es ____ shall ____ pro - claim

all the earth re - peat the loud___ A - men.

Till moons shall wax and wane no more.
With ev - 'ry morn - ing sac - ri - fice.
Their ear - ly bless - ings on his name.

4. Blessings abound where'er he reigns;
   The prisoner leaps to lose his chains,
   The weary find eternal rest,
   And all the sons of want are blest.

5. Let ev'ry creature rise and bring
   Peculiar honours to our King;
   Angels descend with songs again,
   And earth repeat the loud Amen.

✻ Alternative harmonization, stanza 5, bars 9-10

An - gels de - scend with

88. Neighbours
(Fill us with your love)

Tom Colvin and friends in Ghana

'Chereponi'
Ghana folk song
Arr. Betty Pulkingham

Simply, gently

Refrain

Je - su,_____ Je - su,_____ fill us with your love, show

Fine

us how to serve the neigh-bours we have from you.

1. Kneels at the feet of his friends,   si - lent - ly wash - es their
2. Neigh-bours are rich folk and poor,   neigh-bours are black, brown and
3. These are the ones we should serve,   these are the ones we should
4. Lov - ing puts us on our knees,   ser - ving as though we were

D. C.

feet,   mas-ter who acts as a slave____ to them.____
white,   neigh-bours are near-by and far____ a - way.____
love.   All these are neighbours to us____ and you.____
slaves,   this is the way we should live____ with you.____

This folk song may be sung in four-part harmony, using chords in the right-hand piano part (basses sing melody). Sing the verses in unison. A very effective arrangement is achieved when voices sing alone, and a hand-drum is used to create poly-rhythms.

89. There's a wideness in God's mercy

Frederick William Faber

'Beecher'
John Zundel

Cheerfully

1. There's a wide-ness in God's mer-cy Like the wide-ness of the sea;
2. There is no place where earth's sor-rows Are more felt than up in heav'n;
3. For the love of God is broad-er Than the mea-sure of man's mind;

There's a kind-ness in his jus-tice, Which is more than lib-er-ty.
There is no place where earth's fail-ings Have such kind-ly judg-ment giv'n.
And the heart of the E-ter-nal Is most won-der-ful-ly kind.

There is wel-come for the sin-ner, And more gra-ces for the good;
There is plen-ti-ful re-demp-tion In the blood that has been shed;
If our love were but more sim-ple, We should take him at his word;

There is mer-cy with the Sav-iour; There is heal-ing in his blood.
There is joy for all the mem-bers In the sor-rows of the Head.
And our lives would be all sun-shine In the sweet-ness of the Lord.

90. You are my witnesses

Capo 2 (C)

Betty Pulkingham

With strength, boldly

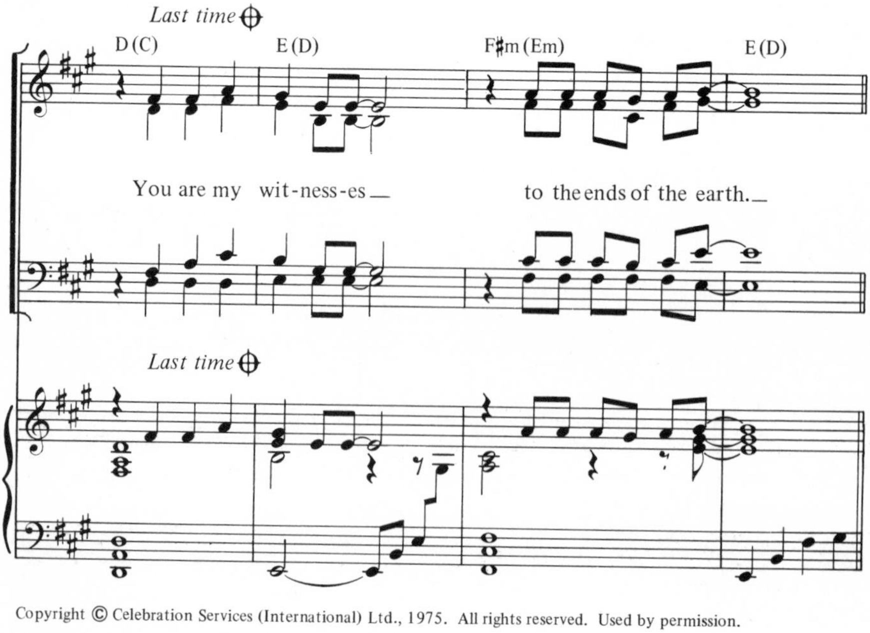

Refrain

[1st time only F#m (Em)]

You are my wit-ness-es __ to the ends of the earth. __

Last time

You are my wit-ness-es __ to the ends of the earth. __

Last time

1. You are my peo-ple I love,——— gen-tle as dove,—
(trebles) 3. You are my trees bear-ing fruit— for peo-ple to eat,——
(men) 4. You are my pro-phets and priests,— pro-claim-ing my feasts,—
6. You are be - lov-ed of God,——— liv-ing his word,—

(men) 2. You are my sons of new birth, liv - ing on earth———
(trebles) 5. You are my shep-herds of sheep, o - ver them keep - -

(1.) wise—— and harm - - less ones.
(3.) tast - ing the good-ness of —— the Lord.
(4.) tell - ing the won - ders— of God.
(6.) dy - ing his death— 'til —— he comes.

(2.)— but born from— on high.
(5.) - - - - ing watch ——— by night.

wit - ness-es _____ to the ends of the earth._____

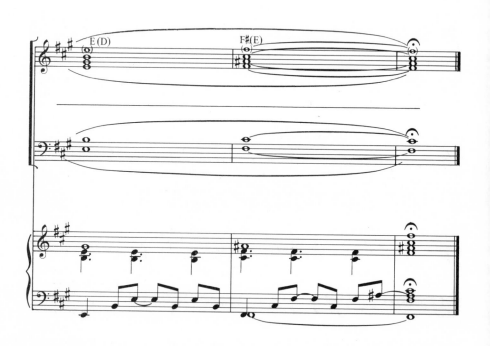

91. Jesus is the one who saves

James Berlucchi
Arr. Charles High

Boldly, with energy

1. All ___ glo - ry to the Fa - ther of life; ___ the
3. Thank you, Je - sus, ___ for ris - ing for us, ___ the

praise be to the Ho - ly Spi - rit, ___
Fa - ther's love com-plete and glo - rious. ___

and to the shin - ing light of this world. ___
Now we claim the vic - t'ry you give to us. ___

Je - sus is the one who saves.——
Je - sus is the one who saves.

Final ending

Je - sus is the one who saves.

Je - sus is the one who saves.

92. Kyrie eleison

Jodi Page Clark

all my peo - - ple, weep with me.'

we will serve them, help them stand.'

take your life in - to the world.

Optional 3-part harmony (SAT)
Refrain

Ky - ri - e e - lei - son, Chris - te e -

lei - son, Ky - ri - e e - le - - - -

Final ending

- - - - i - son.

Final ending

Last time only, refrain may be repeated.

93. Won't you come?

Capo 1 (D)
Based on Luke 14:16-24

Dave Porter

With an easy swing

Come! won't you come, — for the ban - - quet is laid. — Won't you come, — for the feast — is pre-pared.

Won't you come, — won't you come, —

Solo 1. But one man said — he'd bought a house,

Solo 2. But the in-vi-ta-tion — still went out —

(verse 3. ✱)

94. Your love is changing the world

Jon Polce
Arr. Shirley Lewis Brown

SONGS FOR CHILDREN

95. When the Lord came

Kim Miller

American folk melody
Arr. Shirley Lewis Brown

With simplicity

When the Lord came to our land, he was not a wealth-y man.

He was born in pov - er - ty and the {
stars all looked to
an - gels came to
shep - herds came to
wise men came to
don - keys came to
}

*From verse 2 onward repeat these two bars in cumulative fashion, starting with the last verse you have sung and working your way back to the 'brightest star.'

96. Hosanna to the living King!

B. Prout and J. Belt
Arr. Betty Pulkingham

1. I will praise the Lord with harp and string, I will praise the Lord with ev - 'ry - thing; I will praise the Lord with all my heart, and this is how I'll start:
2. I will love the Lord by lov - ing you, I will love the Lord so you'll love him too; I will love the Lord in all I do, for love makes all things new.
3. I will give the Lord the things I bear, I will give the Lord my ev - 'ry care; for I know his love is al - ways there. His prais - es we will share.

Ho - san - na to the liv - ing King, ho - san - na to the Lord! 'Ho-

san - na,'all cre - a - tion sings to you in one ac - cord.

97. Silent night

Joseph Mohr

'Holy Night'
Franz Grueber

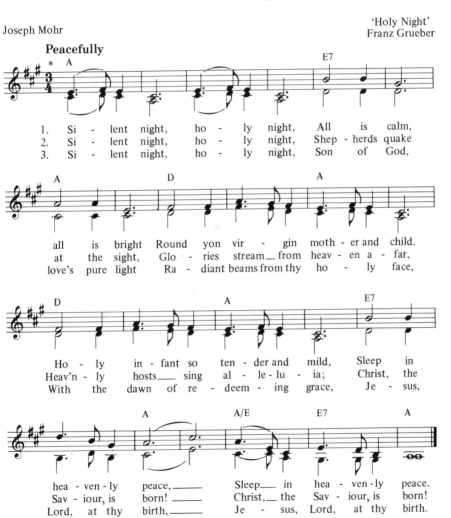

Peacefully

1. Si - lent night, ho - ly night, All is calm,
2. Si - lent night, ho - ly night, Shep - herds quake
3. Si - lent night, ho - ly night, Son of God,

all is bright Round yon vir - gin moth - er and child.
at the sight, Glo - ries stream from heav - en a - far,
love's pure light Ra - diant beams from thy ho - ly face,

Ho - ly in - fant so ten - der and mild, Sleep in
Heav'n - ly hosts sing al - le - lu - ia; Christ, the
With the dawn of re - deem - ing grace, Je - sus,

hea - ven - ly peace, Sleep in hea - ven - ly peace.
Sav - iour, is born! Christ, the Sav - iour, is born!
Lord, at thy birth, Je - sus, Lord, at thy birth.

*The original version of this song was for two-part treble voices and guitar.

98. Five barley loaves

Based on John 6: 1-13

Betty Pulkingham

Sprightly

Refrain

Five bar-ley loaves and two fish - es, five bar-ley loaves and two
fish - es, five bar-ley loaves and two fish - es, it was e-nough for him. *Fine*

1. What __ are __ these a - mong __ so man - y?
2. Give it to the Lord and __ he __ will use it.
3. Took __ the __ bread and __ thanked his Fa - ther.
4. Sent __ it __ down for the peo - ple to eat. __
5. Twelve __ bas - kets __ were __ left o - ver.

What __ are __ these a - mong __ so man - y? What __ are __ these a -
Give it to the Lord and __ he __ will use it. Give it to the Lord and __
Took __ the __ bread and __ thanked his Fa - ther. Took __ the __ bread and __
Sent __ it __ down for the peo-ple to eat. __ Sent __ it __ down for the
Twelve __ bas - kets __ were __ left o - ver. Twelve __ bas - kets __

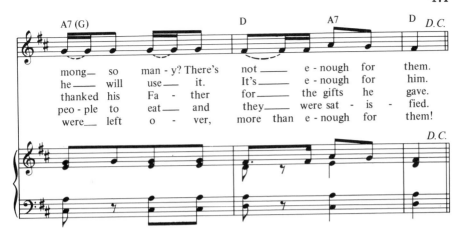

mong—	so	man - y?	There's	not ⎯	e - nough	for	them.
he ⎯	will	use ⎯	it.	It's ⎯	e - nough	for	him.
thanked	his	Fa -	ther	for⎯	the gifts	he	gave.
peo - ple	to	eat ⎯	and	they⎯	were sat - is -		fied.
were⎯	left	o -	ver,	more than	e - nough	for	them!

The story of the loaves and fishes can be mimed by one group of children while others sing the song.
An adventuresome group will enjoy singing the refrain and verse simultaneously — in the manner of a round. (For this purpose use chords indicated in brackets for bars 2 and 6 of the verses.)

99. There's new life in Jesus

Source unknown
Arr. Max Dyer

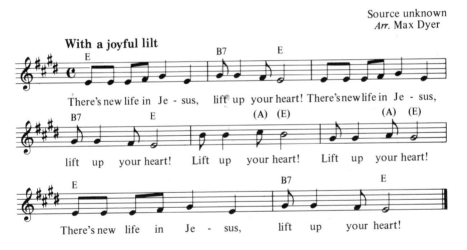

With a joyful lilt

There's new life in Je - sus, lift up your heart! There's new life in Je - sus, lift up your heart! Lift up your heart! Lift up your heart! There's new life in Je - sus, lift up your heart!

Other verses may be added, e.g.

There is healing in his love, lift up your heart! *(repeat)*
Lift up your heart! Lift up your heart!
There is healing in his love, lift up your heart!

There is freedom in his praise, *etc.*

Allelu is good for you, *etc.*

This song is often sung without accompaniment: however, guitar chords have been added for those who prefer to use them.

100. God is for me
(Gud är för mig)

Capo 2 (G)

Swedish melody
Arr. Betty Pulkingham

Bright and happy

God is for me, though I am lit - tle;
Gud är för mig, fast jag är lit - en;

God is for me, though I am dumb.*
Gud är för mig, fast jag är dum.

God is for me, though I am la - zy, or
Gud är för mig, fast jag är slar - vig och

mis - chiev-ous or glad or glum.__
skval - ler - byt - ta, bing, bing - bång.__

*less than brilliant

This delightful Swedish song may be accompanied by hand actions:

God is for me though I am little.

God is for me though I am dumb.

(floppy wrists)

God is for me though I am lazy or mischievous or glad or glum.

Think of it: can you imagine? Think of it: God is for me!

Think of it: can you imagine? God loves even you and me.

101. Peter and James and John

Anon.
Arr. Mimi Farra

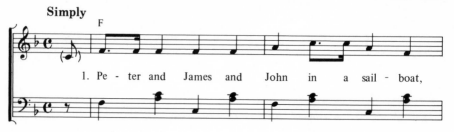

1. Pe - ter and James and John in a sail - boat,

1. Peter and James and John in a sailboat, (3x)   out on the beautiful sea.

(rocking action)

2. They/fished all night   but they caught nothing, (3x)   out on the beautiful sea.

3. A-/long came Jesus walkin' on the seashore, (3x)   out by the beautiful sea.

4. He/said, 'Throw your nets   over on the other side, (3x)   out on the beautiful sea.'

5. The/nets were filled with GREAT BIG FISHES, (3x)   out on the beautiful sea.

6. The/lesson of the story is   listen to the Lord, (3x)   wherever you may be.

102. We must follow the Lord

Fiona Watson (age 11)
Arr. Mimi Farra

We must fol-low the Lord__ in all his ways, __ to-

day and ev-'ry sin-gle day; __ we must show him that we

love__ him, __ our Sav-iour and our King. __

1. He was born on ——— Christ - mas day ——————— to
2. He changed wa - ter in - to wine; ——————— he
3. He was nailed on - to ——— the cross ——————— to
4. He sends his ——— spi - rit to us ——————— so that

live with a poor fam - i - ly. ——————— He worked in a car - pen - ter's shop, —
made the —— blind man see. ——————— He healed the —— sick —— and lame, —
die for —— you and me. ——————— He rose on —— Eas - ter day, —
we can —— share his life. ——————— He makes us —— one fam - i - ly, —

our Sav - iour and our King. ———————

D.C.

103. The seed song

B7 ... **E**

spread a lit - tle love ___ and cheer a - round. ___

root out ___ the weeds of doubt and care. ___
Je - sus ___ Christ di - rects you to. ___

A

Plant a lit - tle kind - ness from a - bove ___ and

Trust God's spi - rit from a - bove ___ to
Pour for - give - ness all a - round ___ and

you'll have a gar - den of love.

nour - ish the seed of love.
you'll have a fruit - ful ground.

Refrain:

One must water, one must weed, one must sow the precious seed.

We'll all work in unity to tend the garden of love.

104. Abba, Father

Cecilie Hobson

Gently

Refrain

p

Love you, love you, Ab - ba, Fa - ther.
Love you, love you, gen - tle Spi - rit.

Fine

Love you, love you, Je - sus, my Lord.
Love you, love you, liv - ing Word.

mp

1. Show me, O Fa -ther, how to be o - be - dient,
2. Teach me, Lord Je - sus, how to be your ser - vant,
3. Fill me, O Spi - rit, with the joy of lov - ing,

D.C.

put - ting your will be - fore my own.
part of your bo - dy here on earth.
giv - ing and shar - ing your life in the world.

105. The instrument song

Sherrell Prebble

Brightly

Let us praise the Lord with guit - ar, let us

praise the Lord with guit - ar. Let all the earth sing

praise to the Lord, let us make a joy - ful sound! Let us

praise the Lord with the tam - bour - ine, let us

Other verses may be sung, e.g. Let us praise the Lord with the piano.
Let us praise the Lord with the bells.

† This bar will become longer as other verses are added, e.g.

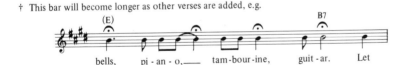

Families will have fun singing this song. Don't be limited to instruments at hand, but include imaginary ones which are easy to imitate and mime (flute, trumpet, drum). 'People' noises are fair game as well: we can praise the Lord 'with our hands' (clap, clap), 'with our feet' (stomp, stomp), or 'with our voices' (lah, lah). For very young children, the 'barnyard' variation is popular, e.g., one can praise the Lord 'like a duck' (quack, quack). We could go on, but we won't!

106. Rain song

Betty Pulkingham

Dreamily

Refrain

Fall - ing, fall - ing, gent - ly fall - ing,
rain from heav'n so gent - ly fall - ing on the earth, so
parched and thirst - y; God sends down his

cresc.

rain.

Final ending

dim.

rain.

An imaginative use of this song with young children involves simple finger play of falling rain.
The song has a peaceful, gentle quality.

107. Jesus loves me

Anna B. Warner vs. 1 and 3 (alternative)

William B. Bradbury
Arr. Betty Pulkingham

Smooth and lyrical

1. Je-sus loves me, this I know, for the Bi-ble tells me so.
2. Je-sus loves the In-dian boy, bow and ar-row for a toy;
3. Je-sus loves the Es-ki-mo in the land of ice and snow;
4. Boys and girls a-cross the seas Je-sus loves as well as me;

Lit-tle ones to him be-long. They are weak, but he is strong.
big Phil'-pi-no, wee Chin-ese, liv-ing far a-cross the seas.
and he loves the cow-boy, too, with his horse and rope las-so.
so our lit-tle friends are they, and with us they all can say:

Refrain

Yes, Je-sus loves me. Yes, Je-sus loves me.

Yes, Je-sus loves me. The Bi-ble tells me so.

Alternative verses to follow verse I.

2. Jesus loves me when I'm good,
   When I do the things I should.
   Jesus loves me when I'm bad,
   Though it makes him very sad.

3. Jesus loves me, he who died,
   Heaven's gates to open wide.
   He will wash away my sin,
   Let this little child come in.

108. Christ the worker

Tr. Tom Colvin

Ghana work song

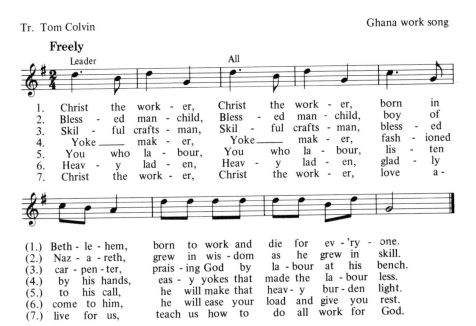

Freely

Leader   All

1. Christ the work - er, Christ the work - er, born in
2. Bless - ed man - child, Bless - ed man - child, boy of
3. Skil - ful crafts - man, Skil - ful crafts - man, bless - ed
4. Yoke___ mak - er, Yoke___ mak - er, fash - ioned
5. You who la - bour, You who la - bour, lis - ten
6. Heav - y lad - en, Heav - y lad - en, glad - ly
7. Christ the work - er, Christ the work - er, love a -

(1.) Beth - le - hem, born to work and die for ev - 'ry - one.
(2.) Naz - a - reth, grew in wis - dom as he grew in skill.
(3.) car - pen - ter, prais - ing God by la - bour at his bench.
(4.) by his hands, eas - y yokes that made the la - bour less.
(5.) to his call, he will make that heav - y bur - den light.
(6.) come to him, he will ease your load and give you rest.
(7.) live for us, teach us how to do all work for God.

109. God is our Father

Capo 3 (D)

Alex Simons
and Freda Kimmey

Rollicking

God is our Fa - - ther, __ for he has
_____ la la _____ la la la

made us his own, __ made Je - sus our broth - - er, __ and
la la la la _____ la la ___ la la ___ la la ___ la

hand in hand we grow to-geth - er as one. _____
la la la la la la la ___ la la la. _____

Fine

Sing praise to the Lord with tam -

In addition to the fun of doing a rhythmic hand-clap and foot-stomp together, the 'la - la' refrain is a wonderful springboard for harmonizing and vocal improvisation.

PSALMS

110. Psalm 8

With joyful abandon

Phil Higgs

111. The Lord's my shepherd

Capo 1 (Em)
Scottish Psalter
Psalm 23

Merla Watson
Arr. Mimi Farra

Lyrical

1. The Lord's my shep - herd, I'll not want. He
2. Yea, though I walk in death's dark vale, yet
3. Good - ness and mer - cy all my life shall

makes me down to lie In pas - tures green: he
will I fear none ill: For thou art with me,
sure - ly fol - low me: And in God's house for

lead-eth me the qui - et wa - ters by.
and thy rod and staff me com - fort still.
ev - er-more my dwell-ing place shall be.

My soul he doth re - store a - gain; and
My ta - ble thou hast fur - nish - ed in
*Hal - le - lu - jah, hal - le - lu - jah, hal -

*The final 'Hallelujah' refrain may be repeated several times with acceleration of tempo. Tambourine or other rhythm instruments add colour.

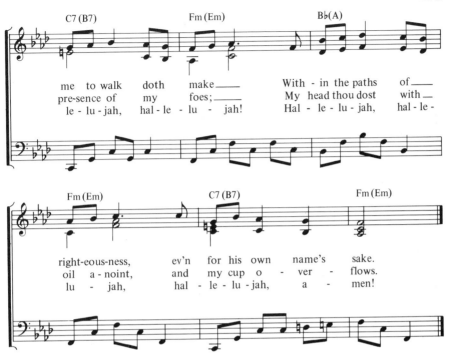

C7 (B7)   Fm (Em)   Bb(A)

me to walk   doth   make____   With - in the paths   of____
pre-sence of   my   foes;____   My head thou dost   with__
le - lu - jah,   hal - le - lu - jah!   Hal - le - lu - jah,   hal - le -

Fm (Em)   C7 (B7)   Fm (Em)

right-eous-ness,   ev'n for his own   name's   sake.
oil a - noint,   and   my cup o - ver - flows.
lu - jah,   hal - le - lu - jah,   a - men!

112. The Lord is my light

(4 - part round)

Psalm 27:1   Shirley Lewis Brown

Simply

The Lord is my light and my sal - va - tion; whom
then shall I fear? The Lord is the strength
of my life; of whom shall I be a - fraid?

113. Israel, rely on Yahweh

Capo 3 (A)
Psalm 131

Mike Fitzgerald
Arr. Charles High

to the Son and Spi - - rit praise,

e -ter -nal praise in end - less peace.

D.C.

114. The Lord is my shepherd
(4 - part round)

Based on Psalm 23

Smoothly

Old Round
Arr. C. Wetzel

The Lord is my shep -herd, my needs are pro - vid - ed; I

rest in green pas - tures be - side the still wa - ters.

2. He strengthens my spirit; I walk without fearing,
For he is beside me to guide and protect me.

3. My table is spread where his peace is around me;
He soothes me with oil, and my cup runneth over.

4. Surely / goodness and love will ever be with me,
And I shall abide in his presence forever.

115. Those who trust in the Lord

Based on Psalm 125

John Smith
Arr. Mimi Farra

Slow and sustained

1. Those who trust in the Lord are like Mount
2. As the moun-tains are a-bout, are a-bout Je-
3. Peace be on Is-ra-el, peace be on
4. Al-le-lu-ia, al-le-lu, al-le-lu-ia,

Zion which shall ne-ver be re-moved,
ru-sa-lem, so the Lord is 'round a-bout,
Is-ra-el, peace be on Is-ra-el
al-le-lu, al-le-lu-ia, al-le-lu,

and shall re-main for ev-er.
'round his peo-ple here.
now and for ev-er-more.
al-le-lu-ia.

*May be sung, or played (on solo instrument) as a 2-part round.

116. Sing unto the Lord

Psalm 96: 1, 2, 4, 7, 11

Linda Spencer
Arr. Betty Pulkingham

Joyfully, well-accented

Lord, all the earth.

Sing un-to the Lord, bless his name, sing— un-to him. Sing un-to the Lord, sing— a new song.

Fine

1. For the Lord is great and greatly to be
2. Give unto the Lord all the glory due his
3. Let the heav'ns rejoice and let the earth be

praised.
name;
glad;

We lift our hearts, and with our voices
for his love he's
for he comes a-

praise.
shown, and to the earth he came.
gain, and a new song we now have.

117. I will dwell in his secret place

Capo 2 (C)
Based on Psalm 91

Gail Cole and
Glen Cummings
Arr. Shirley Lewis Brown

In his for - tress I will take ref - uge,

in my God, the Most High.

Fine

unison

1. From plague and from snare you are pro - tect - ed;
2. There shall no e - vil o'er-come you,
3. When I call to the Lord he will ans - wer.

118. Jubilate, everybody

Capo 5 (Am)
Psalm 100

Fred Dunn
Arr. Celia Harrisson

With vigour

Ju - bi-la - te, ev - 'ry-bo - dy, serve the Lord_ in __ all your ways, and come be-fore his pres-ence sing - ing; en - ter now_ his_ courts with praise. For the Lord our God is gra - cious, and his mer - cy ev - er-last - ing. Ju - bi-la - te, ju - bi-la - te, ju - bi-la - te De - o!

119. Thy lovingkindness

Capo 1 (E)
From Psalm 63

Anon.
Verses Jan Harrington
Arr. Mimi Farra

In moderate time

Refrain

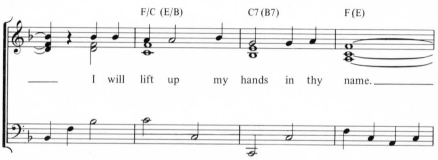

I will lift up my hands in thy name.

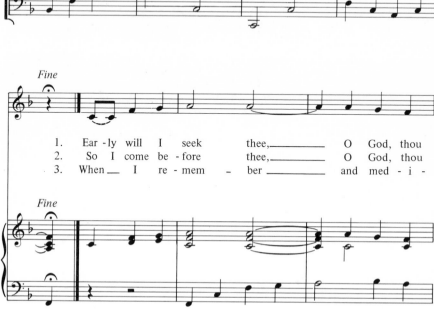

Fine

1. Ear-ly will I seek thee,_____ O God, thou
2. So I come be-fore thee,_____ O God, thou
3. When I re-mem – ber _____ and med - i -

art my God; ear-ly will I seek thee,_____
art my God; so I come be - fore thee,_____
tate on thee; when I re-mem - ber _____

If the refrain is used without the verses, it may be lengthened (by repetition) to the words:

'I lift my hands up unto thy name. (2x)
My lips shall praise thee, thus will I bless thee,
I will lift up my hands in thy name.'

120. Jubilate Deo

Psalm 100

Jonathan Asprey

Bright and rhythmical

Refrain

O_____ be joy-ful in the Lord!__ O__ be joy-ful in__the

Lord! Let us make a joy-ful noise, let the whole earth re - joice!_____

_____ O be joy - ful in the Lord, all__ye lands!_____

1. Know that the Lord he is God:_____
3. Know that the Lord he is good:_____

2. En - ter his gates with thanks-giv - ing:__

121. Come and bless the Lord

Capo 3 (E)
Psalm 134

Graeme Wise
Arr. Mimi Farra

Gently, flowing

On the words 'Lift up your hands in the sanctuary' one can do just that, finishing off this simple hand movement with two light claps (see bar 10).

122. I lift up my soul

D tuning (DADGBE)
Capo 3 (D)
Based on Psalm 25

Tim Manion
Arr. Betty Pulkingham

Cm7 (Am7)   F (D)

1. Yah - weh,_____ show your ways to me._____

2. The Lord is so good, so ho - ly,_____

3. All day long I hope in your good-ness,_____ re -

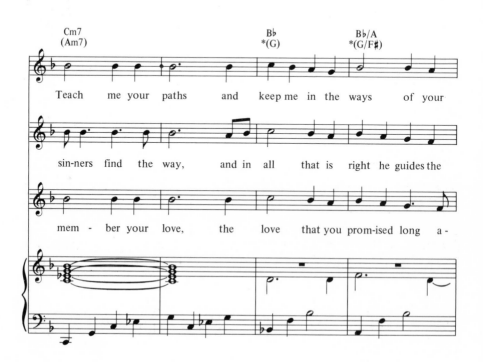

Cm7 (Am7)   Bb *(G)   Bb/A *(G/F#)

Teach me your paths and keep me in the ways of your

sin-ners find the way, and in all that is right he guides the

mem - ber your love, the love that you prom-ised long a -

truth, _____ for you are the God that saves me. __

hum-ble. _____ The poor he leads in his path-ways. __

go, _____ and the kind-ness that you gave from of old. __

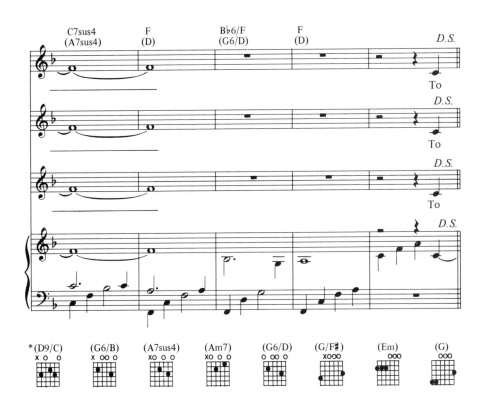

123. Lift up your heads

Psalm 24

Michelle Stoodley
Arr. Mimi Farra

Original choral arrangement available is song book 'With Thanksgiving', pub. Mustard Seed Recordings, 36 Mill Lane, York YO3 7TE, England.

124. Psalm 84

(How lovely is thy dwelling-place)

D tuning (DADF#AD)
Capo 3 (D)

Traditional Scottish folk melody
Arr. Jonathan Asprey

1. and 4. How lovely is thy dwelling-place,
2. Even the sparrow finds a home
3. And I'd rather be a door-keeper

vs. 2 †he can settle

O Lord of hosts, to me. My
where †he can settle down. And the
and only stay a day, than

vs. 2

F (D)
† hap-py are

F Maj7 (D Maj7)   Bb9 (G9)

How love - ly   is   thy   dwell-ing place,   O
And †happy   are   those who are   dwell-ing where   the
and   no   good   thing   does   he with-hold   from

C7 (A7)   F (D)   F Maj7 (D Maj7)

Lord   of   hosts,   to   me.
song   of   praise   is   sung.
those who walk   his   way.

Final ending
Bb9 (G9)   F (D)   F Maj7 (D Maj7)   Bb9 (G9)

F (D)   Bb9 (G9)   F (D)

dim.   pp

F (D)   F Maj7 (D Maj7)   Bb9 (G9)   C7 (A7)

SECTION 9

SEASONAL SONGS

125. Come, Holy Ghost

Latin, 9th. cent.
Tr. John Cosin

'Veni, creator Spiritus'
Sarum Plainsong, Mode VIII

In unison, smoothly

1. Come, Ho - ly Ghost, our souls in-spire, And light-en with ce - les - tial fire;
2. Thy bless - ed unc - tion from a - bove Is com-fort, life, and fire of love;
3. A - noint and cheer our soil - ed face With the a - bun-dance of thy grace;
4. Teach us to know the Fa - ther, Son, And thee, of Both, to be but One;

Thou the a - noint-ing Spi - rit art, Who dost thy seven-fold gifts im-part.
En - a - ble with per - pet - ual light The dul-ness of our blind - ed sight.
Keep far our foes, give peace at home; Where thou art guide no ill can come.
That through the a - ges all a - long This may be our end - less song,

(4.) 'Praise to thy e - ter - nal mer-it, Fa - ther, Son, and Ho - ly Spi-rit.'

126. Christ the Lord is risen today

Charles Wesley

'Gwalchmai'
J. D. Jones
Descant Betty Pulkingham

As a carol

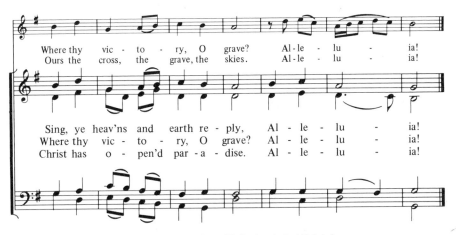

Where thy vic - to - ry, O grave? Al - le - lu - ia!
Ours the cross, the grave, the skies. Al - le - lu - ia!

Sing, ye heav'ns and earth re - ply, Al - le - lu - ia!
Where thy vic - to - ry, O grave? Al - le - lu - ia!
Christ has o - pen'd par - a - dise. Al - le - lu - ia!

4. Soar we now where Christ has led, Alleluia!
Following our exalted Head; Alleluia!
Made like him, like him we rise, Alleluia!
Ours the cross, the grave, the skies. Alleluia!

127. Good morning, this is the day

David McKeithen

Bright and cheerful

1. Good mor - ning, this is__ the day;____ good mor - ning,
2. We will re - joice and be glad;____ we will re -
3. Christ__ is ris - en__ to - day;____ Christ__ is

this is__ the day;____ good mor - ning, this is__ the
joice and be glad;____ we will re - joice and be
ris - en__ to - day;____ Christ__ is ris - en__ to -

day, which__ the Lord has made.____
glad, lift up our hands and praise his name.____
day. Al - le - lu - ia, al - le - lu ia!____

128. The sorrow of Mary

Latin, 13th century

'Dolorosa'
Shirley Lewis Brown

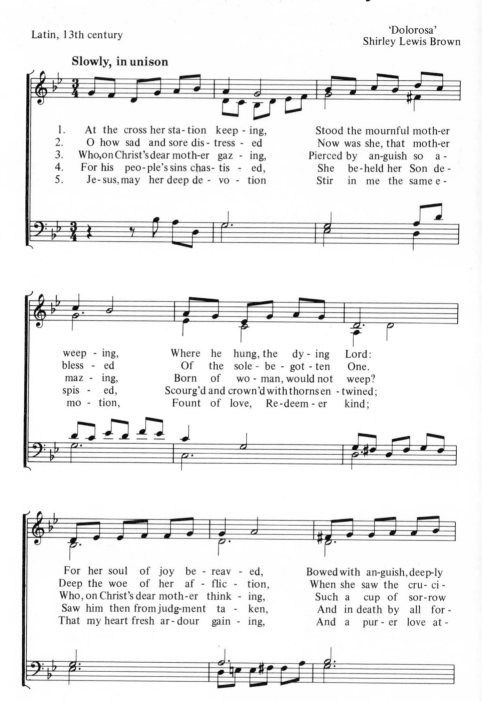

Slowly, in unison

1. At the cross her sta-tion keep-ing, Stood the mournful moth-er weep-ing, Where he hung, the dy-ing Lord: For her soul of joy be-reav-ed, Bowed with an-guish, deep-ly
2. O how sad and sore dis-tress-ed Now was she, that moth-er bless-ed Of the sole-be-got-ten One. Deep the woe of her af-flic-tion, When she saw the cru-ci-
3. Who, on Christ's dear moth-er gaz-ing, Pierced by an-guish so a-maz-ing, Born of wo-man, would not weep? Who, on Christ's dear moth-er think-ing, Such a cup of sor-row
4. For his peo-ple's sins chas-tis-ed, She be-held her Son de-spis-ed, Scourg'd and crown'd with thorns en-twined; Saw him then from judg-ment ta-ken, And in death by all for-
5. Je-sus, may her deep de-vo-tion Stir in me the same e-mo-tion, Fount of love, Re-deem-er kind; That my heart fresh ar-dour gain-ing, And a pur-er love at-

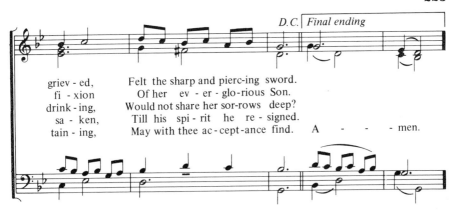

griev - ed,   Felt the sharp and pierc-ing sword.
fi - xion   Of her ev - er - glo-rious Son.
drink - ing,   Would not share her sor-rows deep?
sa - ken,   Till his spi - rit he re - signed.
tain - ing,   May with thee ac-cept-ance find. A - - - men.

129. Man of sorrows

Philipp Bliss

With breadth

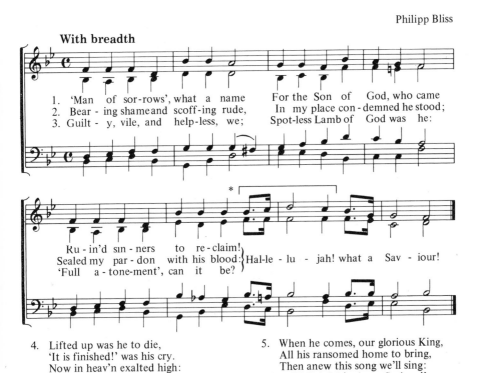

1. 'Man of sor-rows', what a name   For the Son of God, who came
2. Bear - ing shame and scoff-ing rude,   In my place con-demned he stood;
3. Guilt - y, vile, and help-less, we;   Spot-less Lamb of God was he:

Ru - in'd sin - ners to re-claim!
Sealed my par-don with his blood: } Hal-le - lu - jah! what a Sav - iour!
'Full a-tone-ment', can it be?

4. Lifted up was he to die,
'It is finished!' was his cry.
Now in heav'n exalted high:
Hallelujah! what a Saviour!

5. When he comes, our glorious King,
All his ransomed home to bring,
Then anew this song we'll sing:
'Hallelujah! what a Saviour!'

*In stanzas 3, 4 and 5 'Hallelujah' may be repeated (even twice) as the sense of exultation grows.

130. Lo! he comes

Charles Wesley

'South College'
Betty Pulkingham

With majesty

1. Lo! he comes, with clouds de - scend - ing,
2. Ev - 'ry eye shall now be - hold him,
3. Those dear to - kens of his pas - sion
4. Yea, a - men! Let all a - dore thee,

once for our sal - va - tion slain; Thou - sand, thou-sand
robed in dread-ful maj - es - ty; Those who set at
still his daz -zling bo - dy bears; Cause of end - less
high on thine e - ter - nal throne; Sav - iour, take the

(Men)

saints at - tend -ing swell the tri -umph of his train. Al - le -
naught and sold him, pierced and nail'd him to the tree. Deep - ly
ex - ul - ta - tion to his ran-som'd wor - ship - pers. With what
power and glo - ry; claim the king-dom for thine own: Al - le -

(Trebles)   (Men)   (Trebles)

lu - ia, al - le - lu - ia, al - le - lu - ia, al - le -
wail - ing, deep - ly wail - ing, deep - ly wail - ing, deep - ly
rap - ture, with_ what rap - ture, with_ what rap - ture, with_ what
lu - ia, al - le - lu - ia, al - le - lu - ia, al - le -

(All)

lu - ia, Christ the Lord re - turns____ to reign.
wail - ing, Shall the true Mes - si - ah see.
rap - ture Gaze we on those glo - rious scars.
lu - ia, Thou shalt reign, and thou____ a - lone.

131. Dona nobis pacem

(Grant us thy peace)

Sustained and quiet   Traditional round

Do - na no - bis pa - cem, pa-cem. Do - na no - bis pa - -
cem. Do - na no - bis pa-cem. Do - na no-bis pa - - cem.
Do - na no - bis pa-cem. Do-na no-bis pa - - cem.

132. Hosanna, Lord!

Capo 2 (G)

Mimi Farra

Brightly

Refrain

We cry, 'Ho - san - na, Lord,' yes, 'Ho - san - na, Lord,' yes, 'Ho-
san - na, Lord,' to __ you. We cry, 'Ho - san - na, Lord,' yes, 'Ho-
san - na, Lord,' yes, 'Ho - san - na, Lord,' __ to you.

1. Be - hold, our Sav - iour comes. Be - hold the Son of our
3. He comes to set us free.

2. Child - ren wave their palms as the King of all __ kings rides __
(3.) He gives __ us lib - er -

descant for refrain
(This descant is most effective when sung by higher men's voices.)

One way to enhance the sense of participation in this praise-filled procession is (beginning vs. 2) to wave imaginary palm branches by raising hands in graceful left-to-right movements.

133. The Pentecost song

Based on Joel 2:28-32

Diane Davis Andrew

Boldly, with strength

I will pour out my Spi-rit up-on all__ flesh.____

__ I will __ Cry out to the na - tions;____ tell them I have pro - mised__ I will pour out my Spi-rit up-on all__ flesh_____ 1. Your

G   Am Am9 Am   G

(1.) sons and your daughters will pro - phe-sy, ___ your young men shall see
(2.) All man - kind will know ___ me; ___ they will call me by my
(3.) Come and see the signs I give, ___ dar-kened sun, ___

Am   G   Am Am9 Am

(1.) vis - ions,   your old men will dream dreams. ___
(2.) name.   I will live a - mong ___ them, ___
(3.) moon to blood. ___ Be - hold I am the Lord your God; ___ is

G   Am Am9 Am Am9 Am   D.C.

(1.) In those days ___ I will pour ___ out my Spi - rit. ___
(2.) teach-ing them ___ to walk ___ in my ways. ___
(3.) an - y - thing ___ too hard ___ for ___ me? ___

D.C.

134. Robed in majesty

Capo 2 (A)
Maggie Durran

Diane Davis Andrew

135. Before thy throne, O God

William B. Carpenter

'St. Petersburg'
Arr. from Dmitri Bortniansky

With simple dignity

1. Be - fore thy throne, O God, we kneel; Give us a con - science
2. Search out our hearts and make us true, Wish - ful to give to
3. For sins of heed - less word and deed, For pride am - bi - tious
4. Let the fierce fires which burn and try, Our in - most spi - rits

quick to feel, A rea - dy mind to un - der - stand The
all their due; From love of plea - sure, lust of gold, From
to suc - ceed, For craft - y trade and sub - tle snare To
pu - ri - fy: Con - sume the ill; purge out the shame; O

mean - ing of thy chast - 'ning hand; What - e'er the pain and
sins which make the heart grow cold, Wean us and train us
catch the sim - ple un - a - ware, For lives be - reft of
God, be with us in the flame; A new - born peo - ple

shame may be, Bring us, O Fa - ther, near - er thee.
with thy rod; Teach us to know our faults, O God.
pur - pose high, For - give, for - give, O Lord, we cry.
may we rise, More pure, more true, more no - bly wise. A - men.

136. Arise, shine!

Adapted from Isaiah 60

Eric Glass
Arr. Mimi Farra

With strength

1. Be - hold, the dark - ness shall cov - er the earth, and
2. The gen - tiles shall come to thy light, and
3. Lift up thine eyes round a - bout and see, they
4. Then shalt thou see and flow to-geth - er, and thy
5. The sun shall no more go down, nei-ther shall the

gross dark - ness the peo - ple; But the
kings to the bright-ness of thy ri - sing. And
gath - er them-selves to - geth - er. And
heart shall be en - larged; The a -
moon with - draw it - self; But the

Lord shall a - rise up - on thee, and his
they shall call thee 'the ci - ty of the Lord, the
they shall come, thy sons from a - far, and thy
bun-dance of the sea is con - vert - ed un - to thee, and the
Lord shall be thine ev - er - last - ing light, and the

glo - ry shall be seen__ up - - on thee. _____
Zi - on of the Ho - ly One of Is - ra - el'. _____
daugh - ters shall be nursed__ at thy side. _____
na - tions shall come__ un - to thee. _____
days__ of thy mourn-ing shall be end - ed. _____

Refrain

A - rise, shine; for thy light is come, and the

glo - ry of the Lord is ris - en. _____ Oh, a -

rise,　　　　shine;　for　thy　light　is　　　come,　and　the

glo - ry　of　the　Lord　is　up - on　　thee.——————

Hand movements can enhance the corporate expression of praise in this song:

Arise,　shine;　　for thy light is come, and the glory of the Lord is risen.

Oh, arise,　shine;　　for thy light is come, and the glory of the Lord is upon thee.

137. Bethlehem song

Wiley Beveridge
and Glenna J. McLane

Wiley Beveridge
Arr. Mimi Farra

Gently, not too slow

1. In the lit - tle town＿＿ of Beth - le - hem long a -
2. In a man - ger lay＿＿ this babe of love through the
3. Wise men, ox and ass, ＿＿ come join the praise of his

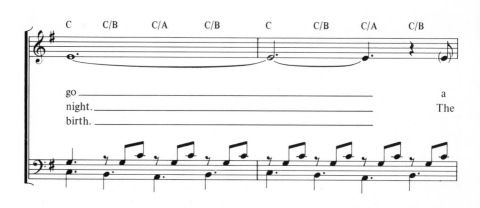

go ＿＿＿＿＿＿＿＿＿ a
night. ＿＿＿＿＿＿＿＿＿ The
birth. ＿＿＿＿＿＿＿＿＿

lit - tle babe＿ was born＿＿ to save the world from all
shep - herds came＿ in joy＿＿ and haste to see God's own
Child - ren of＿ the light＿＿ pro - claim good news to the

138. My Lord, he is a-comin' soon

Capo 2 (Dm)
Laura Winnen

Jeff Cothran

With a slow 'blues' swing: one beat to a bar

Refrain

My Lord, he is a-com-in'___ soon;___ pre-pare ye the way of the Lord.___ Get ev-'ry-thing rea - dy for___ that day;___ pre-pare ye the way of the Lord.___

139. A joyful song

Colleen O'Meara
(age 6)
Arr. Betty Pulkingham

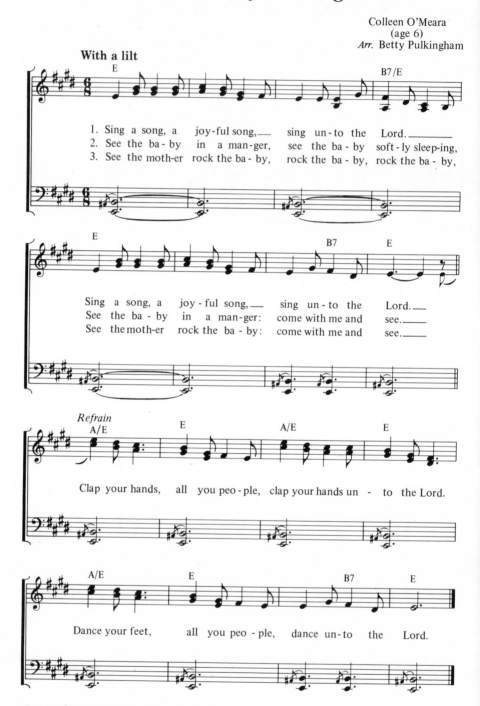

With a lilt

1. Sing a song, a joy-ful song,— sing un-to the Lord.———
2. See the ba-by in a man-ger, see the ba-by soft-ly sleep-ing,
3. See the moth-er rock the ba-by, rock the ba-by, rock the ba-by,

Sing a song, a joy-ful song,— sing un-to the Lord.—
See the ba-by in a man-ger: come with me and see.—
See the moth-er rock the ba-by: come with me and see.—

Refrain

Clap your hands, all you peo-ple, clap your hands un - to the Lord.

Dance your feet, all you peo-ple, dance un-to the Lord.

4. Hear the donkey hee and hawing, hee and hawing, hee and hawing,
   Hear the donkey hee and hawing: come with me and see.

5. Shepherds on the hills a-watching, hills a-watching, hills a-watching,
   Shepherds on the hills a-watching: come with me and see.

6. See the star so brightly shining, brightly shining, brightly shining,
   See the star so brightly shining: come with me and see.

7. Kings upon their camels riding, camels riding, camels riding,
   Kings upon their camels riding, bringing gifts to him.

This song appeals to young children, and the verses lend themselves to simple miming by a group of children and leader. Gather the children together on verse 1, dance the refrain in a circle as pictured below:

(The above is a Scottish dance style 'set'.)

Ideas for verses include 'see the baby' (pointing to manger); 'softly sleeping' (tilt head and rest it on folded hands); 'rock the baby' (make a cradle of your arms); 'hear the donkey' (one hand cupped over ear); 'hee and hawing' (place hands straight up on either side of head to form donkey ears).

140. Christmas lullaby

Jodi Page Clark
Arr. Shirley Lewis Brown

Gently rocking

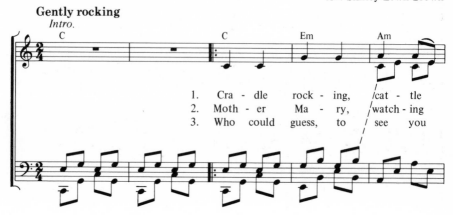

1. Cra - dle rock - ing, /cat - tle
2. Moth - er Ma - ry, /watch - ing
3. Who could guess, to / see you

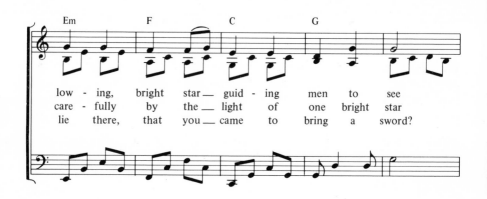

low - ing, bright star — guid - ing men to see
care - fully by the — light of one bright star
lie there, that you — came to bring a sword?

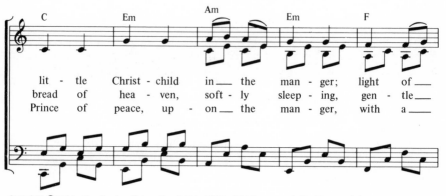

lit - tle Christ - child in — the man - ger; light of —
bread of hea - ven, soft - ly sleep - ing, gen - tle —
Prince of peace, up - on — the man - ger, with a —

all the world to be.
gift of God to man.
price up - on your soul.

Refrain
Hal - le - lu - - - jah, ho - ly child. ___ Ho - san - - na in the high - - est. Glo - ri - a, ___ Em-man - u - el. ___ Ho - san - - - na in the high - est. ___

Fine

4. Do you know, so weak and helpless,
   of the grace you bear to us?
   Do you dream yet of the kingdom
   you will some day bring to pass?

141. ¡Resucitó, resucitó!*

Capo 3 (Em)
Tr. Susan Abbott

Kiko Argüello
Arr. Betty Pulkingham

Joyfully
Refrain

iRe - su - ci - tó,_____ re - su - ci - tó,_____ re - su - ci -
ya,_____ a - le - lu - ya,_____ a - le - lu -

tó,_____ a - le - lu - ya!_____ ¡A - le - lu -
ya,_____ re - su - ci - tó!_____

1. Death,_____ where _ is
2. Re - joice_____ and be hap - py to -
3. If with him we die,_____ with him _ we

*He arose!

142. Hymn to the Spirit

John Richards

'All for Jesus'
John Stainer
Descant Betty Pulkingham

Boldly, with movement

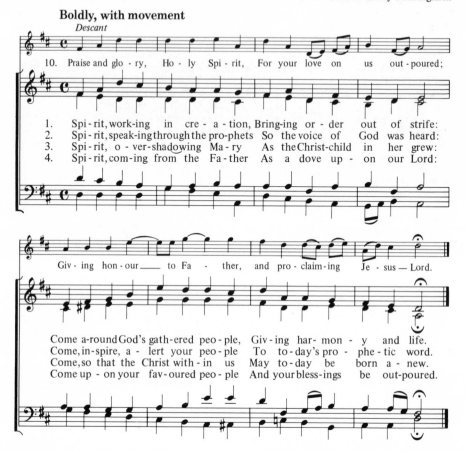

10. Praise and glo - ry, Ho - ly Spi - rit, For your love on us out - poured;

1. Spi - rit, work-ing in cre - a - tion, Bring-ing or - der out of strife:
2. Spi - rit, speak-ing through the pro - phets So the voice of God was heard:
3. Spi - rit, o - ver-shadowing Ma - ry As the Christ-child in her grew:
4. Spi - rit, com-ing from the Fa - ther As a dove up - on our Lord:

Giv - ing hon - our to Fa - ther, and pro - claim-ing Je - sus — Lord.

Come a-round God's gath-ered peo - ple, Giv - ing har - mon - y and life.
Come, in-spire, a - lert your peo - ple To to-day's pro - phe - tic word.
Come, so that the Christ with - in us May to-day be born a - new.
Come up - on your fav-oured peo - ple And your bless-ings be out-poured.

5. Spirit, driving to the desert
   Even God's Anointed One:
   Come to us in trial and testing
   That God's will in us be done.

6. Spirit, bringing freedom, blessing,
   Help to poor, and health to lame:
   Come, anoint us, that such wonders
   May be done in Jesus' Name.

*7. Spirit, taking, breaking, making
   Bread and wine our heavenly food:
   Come, and take us, break us, make us,
   Live Christ's life in us renewed.

*for Holy Communion

8. Spirit, breathed on the disciples,
   Giving peace where there was fear:
   Come among us, touch us, send us,
   Making Jesus' presence near.

9. Spirit, wind and flame, empow'ring
   Fearless witness to the lost:
   Come, unite, 'renew your wonders
   As of a new Pentecost!'

10. Praise and glory, Holy Spirit,
   For your love on us outpoured:
   Giving honour to the Father,
   And proclaiming Jesus — Lord.

Topical Index

CREATION

Awake, awake to love and work	48
How great thou art	80
Hymn to the Spirit	142
I will rejoice	21
Jerusalem is fair	72
Jesus shall reign	87
Morning Psalm	1
Psalm 8	110
Rain song	106
The celebration song	71
The seed song	103
This, this is the day	14

DISCIPLESHIP, SERVANTHOOD

Abba, Father	104
Awake, awake to love and work	48
Be like your Father	67
Children at your feet	66
Christ the worker	108
Everybody song	86
Harvest of righteousness	69
I will rejoice	21
Kyrie eleison	92
Lord, give us your Spirit	52
Tell out, my soul	19
The servant song	70
We must follow the Lord	102
Won't you come?	93
You are my witnesses	90

FAITH, VICTORY

Alabaré	4
All the riches of his grace	30
Awake, O sleeper	79
Christ the Lord is risen today	126
Fear not, for I have redeemed you	49
Five barley loaves	98
For you are my God	77
Great is thy faithfulness	78
Hallelujah . . . our God reigns	24
He's able	73
How great thou art	80
I know whom I have believed	81
I will rejoice	21
I will sing of the mercies	76
Jesus came	38
Jesus, you're a wonder	31
'Lu-ia, 'lu-ia	53
Lift up your heads	123
Living Lord	83
Man of sorrows	129
My sheep hear my voice	60
O for a thousand tongues	23

O love, how deep	75
On Christ the solid rock	82
Peace, perfect peace	41
Peter and James and John	101
¡Resucitó, resucitó!	141
Robed in majesty	134
Tell my people	50
The Lord is my light	112
The Lord is my shepherd	114
The Lord's my shepherd	111
There's a new song in the land	54
There's new life in Jesus	99
Trust in the Lord	43
When led by the Spirit	85
Whosoever will	74

HERITAGE

Arise, shine!	136
Before the Lord Jehovah's throne	13
For you are my God	77
Great is thy faithfulness	78
Hymn to the Spirit	142
In the presence of your people	20
Iona Gloria	12
Israel, rely on Yahweh	113
Jerusalem is fair	72
Lift up your heads	123
People of God	57
Praise, my soul, the King of heaven	18
Those who trust in the Lord	115

HOPE

Alleluia, he is coming	36
Arise, shine!	136
Awake, awake to love and work	48
Children at your feet	66
Fear not, for I have redeemed you	49
For you are my God	77
I will arise and go to Jesus	40
Jerusalem is fair	72
Lo! he comes	130
'Lu-ia, 'lu-ia	53
Peace, perfect peace	41
Praise God for the body	61
Pure light	51
Tell out, my soul	19
The bridegroom's song	44
The Pentecost song	133
There's new life in Jesus	99
Trust in the Lord	43
You are my witnesses	90
Your love is changing the world	94

KINGDOM

Be like your Father	67
Broken for me	68
Children at your feet	66
Christ the worker	108
For you are my God	77
Gift of finest wheat	59
God is our Father	109
Good evening, Father	62
Harvest of righteousness	69
How much greater	64
Jerusalem is fair	72
Jesus is our King	55
Jesus shall reign	87
My sheep hear my voice	60
Neighbours	88
People of God	57
Praise God for the body	61
The celebration song	71
The fishermen	56
The Lord's prayer	63
The seed song	103
The servant song	70
We are coming, Lord	65
We must follow the Lord	102
You are my witnesses	90

LIFE OF JESUS

A joyful song	139
Alleluia, he is coming	36
Bethlehem song	137
Christ the Lord is risen today	126
Christ the worker	108
Five barley loaves	98
Man of sorrows	129
O love, how deep	75
We must follow the Lord	102

MERCY

All the riches of his grace	30
Be like your Father	67
Fear not, for I have redeemed you	49
Great is thy faithfulness	78
I know whom I have believed	81
I will sing of the mercies	76
Morning Psalm	1
People of God	57
Praise, my soul, the King of heaven	18
There's a river of praise	15
There's a wideness in God's mercy	89

OUTREACH

Alabaré	4
Arise, shine!	136
Everybody song	86
Fill my cup, Lord	45
Jesus is the one who saves	91

Jesus shall reign	87
Kyrie eleison	92
Lord, give us your Spirit	52
Neighbours	88
O for a thousand tongues	23
There's a new song in the land	54
There's a wideness in God's mercy	89
There's a new life in Jesus	99
When led by the Spirit	85
Whosoever will	74
Won't you come?	93
You are my witnesses	90
Your love is changing the world	94

PRAISE AND THANKSGIVING

Alabaré	4
Arise, shine!	136
Awake, awake to love and work	48
Before the Lord Jehovah's throne	13
Clap your hands	16
Come and bless the Lord	121
Everybody song	86
Fill your heart with love	17
For you are my God	77
God is our Father	109
Good evening, Father	62
Good morning, Jesus	6
Good morning, this is the day	127
Hallelujah . . . our God reigns	24
Hallelujah song	7
Harvest of righteousness	69
Hosanna, Lord!	132
Hosanna to the living King!	96
How great thou art	80
How much greater	64
Hymn of glory	11
I will rejoice	21
I will sing of the mercies	76
In the presence of your people	20
Iona Gloria	12
Jesus came	38
Jesus is our King	55
Jesus shall reign	87
Jubilate Deo	120
Jubilate Deo (round)	10
Jubilate, everybody	118
Lift up your heads	123
Lo! he comes	130
'Lu-ia, 'lu-ia	53
Morning Psalm	1
O clap your hands	5
O for a thousand tongues	23
O love, how deep	75
People of God	57
Praise, my soul, the King of heaven	18
Praise ye the Lord	3

Psalm 8 110
¡Resucitó, resucitó! 141
Sing to our Father 9
Sing unto the Lord 116
Tell out, my soul 19
The bridegroom's song 44
The celebration song 71
The instrument song 105
The Lord is present 8
There's a new song in the land 54
There's a river of praise........... 15
There's new life in Jesus 99
This, this is the day 14
We want to bless you 2
When I survey the wondrous cross .. 28
When led by the Spirit 85

PRAYER, MEDITATION
Abba, Father 104
Before thy throne, O God 135
Children at your feet 66
Come, Holy Ghost............... 125
Gift of finest wheat 59
Hymn to the Spirit 142
I lift up my soul.................. 122
I will arise and go to Jesus 40
I will dwell in his secret place 117
Israel, rely on Yahweh 113
Jesus 27
Jesus is Lord, alleluia 33
Lord, give us your Spirit 52
Peace, perfect peace 41
Pure light...................... 51
Rain song 106
The Lord's prayer 63
They that wait upon the Lord....... 46
Those who trust in the Lord 115
Trust in the Lord 43
When I survey the wondrous cross .. 28

REPENTANCE
Abba, Father 104
Alleluia, he is coming 36
Before thy throne, O God 135
Come, Lord Jesus 47
I will arise and go to Jesus 40
Kyrie eleison.................... 92
My Lord, he is a-comin' soon 138
The Lord's prayer 63
The sorrow of Mary 128
When I survey the wondrous cross .. 28

THE SPIRIT
Come, Holy Ghost............... 125
Hymn to the Spirit 142
Lord, give us your Spirit 52
Rain song 106
The Pentecost song 133

When led by the Spirit 85

TRINITY
Abba, Father 104
Ballad of the dance 84
Come, Holy Ghost............... 125
Israel, rely on Yahweh 113
Jesus 27
Jesus is the one who saves 91
Jesus, your blood 25
Litany 39
O love, how deep 75
Sing to our Father 9
The celebration song 71

UNITY
Children at your feet 66
Clap your hands 16
Come, Lord Jesus 47
God is our Father 109
Hiney mah tov 58
Hosanna to the living King! 96
How much greater 64
People of God 57
Praise God for the body 61
The seed song 103
The servant song 70
There's a quiet understanding 37
We are coming, Lord 65

WHOLENESS, HEALING
All the riches of his grace 30
Come, Lord Jesus 47
Fill my cup, Lord 45
He's able 73
I will arise and go to Jesus 40
I will dwell in his secret place 117
Israel, rely on Yahweh 113
Jesus, you're a wonder 31
Jesus, your blood 25
Lord, give us your Spirit 52
Morning Psalm 1
O for a thousand tongues 23
Tell my people 50
The Lord's my shepherd 111
There's new life in Jesus 99
When led by the Spirit............. 85
Whosoever will.................. 74
You are my witnesses 90
Your love is changing the world 94

WORSHIP
Abba, Father 104
All the riches of his grace 30
Alleluia, he is coming 36
Before thy throne, O God 135
Bless the holy name of Jesus 32
His name is wonderful 35
I lift up my soul.................. 122

I will arise and go to Jesus 40
I will dwell in his secret place 117
Israel, rely on Yahweh 113
Jesus 27
Jesus is Lord, alleluia 33
Jesus my Saviour 26
Jesus, name above all names 34
Jesus, your blood 25
Jesus, you're a wonder 31
Kyrie eleison 92
Litany 39

Man of sorrows 129
Peace, perfect peace 41
Rain song 106
Tell my people 50
The Lord is present 8
The Lord's prayer 63
There's a quiet understanding 37
Those who trust in the Lord 115
We want to bless you 2
When I survey the wondrous cross . . 28
Worthy the Lamb 29

Worship Leaders' Guide

PART SONGS AND ROUNDS
All the riches of his grace – *2-part
   song* 30
Awake, O sleeper – *4-part round* 79
Dona nobis pacem – *3-part round* . . . 131
Fill your heart with love – *2-part
   round* 17
Five barley loaves – *optional 2-part
   round* 98
Hallelujah song – *2-part song* 7
Hiney mah tov – *2-part round* 58
Iona Gloria – *3-part song* 12
Jesus, your blood – *2-part round* 25
Jubilate Deo – *6-part round* 10
Lo! he comes – *antiphonal* 130
My sheep hear my voice – *6-part
   round* 60
O clap your hands – *2-part song* 5
O for a thousand tongues – *2-part
   song* 23
Praise ye the Lord – *2-part song* 3
The fear of the Lord – *2-part
   round* 42
The Lord is my light – *4-part round* . . 112
The Lord is my shepherd – *4-part
   round* 114
Those who trust in the Lord – *2-part
   round* 115
Whosoever will – *antiphonal* 74
Worthy the Lamb – *3-part round* 29

SPONTANEOUS VERSE SONGS
I will rejoice 21
Jesus, you're a wonder 31
Litany 39
'Lu-ia, 'lu-ia 53
The instrument song 105
There's new life in Jesus 99
Worthy the Lamb 29

HYMNS AND SONGS WITH
DESCANTS
Christ the Lord is risen today 126
For you are my God 77
Hosanna, Lord! 132
Hymn to the Spirit 142
Jesus shall reign 87
O love, how deep 75
Peace, perfect peace 41
Praise, my soul, the King of
   heaven 18
Tell my people 50
When I survey the wondrous cross . . 28

GOOD SONGS FOR CHOIR WITH
CONGREGATION
(Verses may be sung by choir)
Arise, shine! 136
Broken for me 68
Clap your hands 16
Come, Lord Jesus 47
Fear not, for I have redeemed you . . 49
Five barley loaves 98
Harvest of righteousness 69
Hosanna, Lord! 132
I will dwell in his secret place 117
Israel, rely on Yahweh 113
Jesus is our King 55
Jubilate Deo 120
Kyrie eleison 92
Lift up your heads 123
Lord, give us your Spirit 52
Robed in majesty 134
The Pentecost song 133
Trust in the Lord 43
We are coming, Lord 65
You are my witnesses 90
Your love is changing the world 94

USEFUL ARRANGEMENTS FOR CHOIRS

All the riches of his grace 30
Awake, O sleeper 79
Bethlehem song 137
Dona nobis pacem 131
Fear not, for I have redeemed you .. 49
Fill your heart with love 17
For you are my God 77
Gift of finest wheat 59
I will arise and go to Jesus 40
Iona Gloria 12
Jerusalem is fair 72
Jesus my Saviour 26
Morning Psalm 1
Neighbours 88
O for a thousand tongues 23
Praise God for the body 61
Pure light (unison, treble voices) 51
Sing to our Father 9
The servant song 70
The sorrow of Mary 128
There's a river of praise 15
You are my witnesses 90

USEFUL SONGS FOR YOUTH CHOIRS, YOUNG PEOPLE'S GROUPS

Alleluia, he is coming 36
Bethlehem song 137
Clap your hands 16
Everybody song 86
God is our Father 109
Hallelujah song 7
Harvest of righteousness 69
Hiney mah tov 58
How much greater 64
I will rejoice 21
In the presence of your people 20
Jesus is the one who saves 91
Jesus, you're a wonder 31
Jubilate Deo 120
Jubilate, everybody 118
Living Lord 83
'Lu-ia, 'lu-ia 53
My Lord, he is a-comin' soon 138
O clap your hands 5
Psalm 8 110
Psalm 84 124
Sing unto the Lord 116
The bridegroom's song 44
The celebration song 71
The servant song 70
This, this is the day 14
Won't you come? 93

SONGS FOR CHILDREN

Abba, Father 104
Christ the worker 108
Christmas lullaby 140
Everybody song 86
Five barley loaves 98
God is for me 100
God is our Father 109
Good evening, Father 62
Good morning, this is the day 127
Hosanna, Lord! 132
Hosanna to the living King! 96
Jesus came 38
Jesus loves me 107
Neighbours 88
Peter and James and John 101
Praise ye the Lord 3
Rain song 106
The instrument song 105
The seed song 103
We must follow the Lord 102
When the Lord came 95

SONGS WITH MOVEMENT

A joyful song 139
Arise, shine! 136
Clap your hands 16
Come and bless the Lord 121
God is our Father 109
Hosanna, Lord! 132
Peter and James and John 101
The instrument song 105
The Lord's prayer 63
The seed song 103

USEFUL CAMP AND CONFERENCE SONGS

Alabaré 4
Everybody song 86
Fear not, for I have redeemed you .. 49
God is our Father 109
Good evening, Father 62
Good morning, Jesus 6
Good morning, this is the day 127
Hallelujah song 7
He's able 73
Hosanna, Lord! 132
Hymn of glory 11
I will rejoice 21
In the presence of your people 20
Jubilate everybody 118
Praise ye the Lord 3
¡Resucitó, resucitó! 141
Tell my people 50
Tell out, my soul 19
The Lord is present 8
There's a new song in the land 54

There's a river of praise 15
Those who trust in the Lord 115
Thy lovingkindness 119
We want to bless you 2

SONGS WITH INTERNATIONAL APPEAL

A joyful song 139
Alabaré 4
Arise, shine! 136
Christ the worker 108
Dona nobis pacem 131
Hiney mah tov 58
In the presence of your people 20
Iona Gloria 12
Jesus loves me 107
Jesus shall reign 87
'Lu-ia, 'lu-ia 53
My Lord, he is a-comin' soon 138
Neighbours 88
People of God 57
Praise God for the body 61
¡Resucitó, resucitó! 141
Silent night 97
The Lord's my shepherd 111
Those who trust in the Lord 115

SONGS WITH GOOD SOLO VERSES

Ballad of the dance 84
Be like your Father 67
Children at your feet 66
Christmas lullaby 140
Come, Lord Jesus 47
Fear not, for I have redeemed you . . 49
Fill my cup, Lord 45
How great thou art 80
I lift up my soul 122
Israel, rely on Yahweh 113
Kyrie eleison 92
Litany 39
'Lu-ia, 'lu-ia 53
Psalm 84 124
Rain song 106
The seed song 103
Thy lovingkindness 119
Trust in the Lord 43
Won't you come? 93
You are my witnesses 90

SONGS FOR THE LITURGY

ENTRANCE (Introit)

Awake, awake to love and work 48
Come and bless the Lord 121
Jesus shall reign 87
Lift up your heads 123
Morning Psalm 1

Tell out, my soul 19
The Lord is present 8
We want to bless you 2

OFFERTORY

Before the Lord Jehovah's throne . . . 13
Hymn of glory 11
Jesus is our King 55
O for a thousand tongues 23
O love, how deep 75
People of God 57
Praise, my soul, the King of
heaven 18
When I survey the wondrous cross . . 28

COMMUNION

Abba, Father 104
All the riches of his grace 30
Broken for me 68
Gift of finest wheat 59
I will arise and go to Jesus 40
I will dwell in his secret place 117
Jesus is Lord, alleluia 33
Jesus my Saviour 26
Jesus, your blood 25
Peace, perfect peace 41
Those who trust in the Lord 115
We are coming, Lord 65
When I survey the wondrous cross . . 28
Worthy the Lamb 29

SEASONAL SONGS

ADVENT

Awake, O sleeper 79
Before thy throne, O God 135
Lift up your heads 123
Lo! he comes 130
My Lord, he is a-comin' soon 138
The bridegroom's song 44

CHRISTMAS

A joyful song 139
Bethlehem song 137
Christmas lullaby 140
Dona nobis pacem 131
Fill your heart with love 17
Silent night 97
When the Lord came 95

EPIPHANY

Arise, shine! 136
Before the Lord Jehovah's throne . . . 13
Pure light 51

PASSIONTIDE

Alleluia, he is coming 36
Before thy throne, O God 135
Hosanna, Lord! (Palm Sunday) 132

How great thou art 80
Lift up your heads *(Palm Sunday)* . . . 123
Man of sorrows 129
Neighbours *(Maundy Thursday)* 88
O love, how deep 75
The sorrow of Mary *(Good Friday)* . . 128
When I survey the wondrous cross . . 28

EASTER
Alleluia, he is coming 36
Awake, O sleeper 79
Christ the Lord is risen today 126
Clap your hands 16
Good morning, this is the day 127
Hymn of glory 11
¡Resucitó, resucitó! 141
Robed in majesty 134

ASCENSION
Christ the Lord is risen today 126

Jesus my Saviour 26
O clap your hands 5
O love, how deep 75
Robed in majesty 134
You are my witnesses 90

PENTECOST
Come, Holy Ghost 125
Hymn to the Spirit 142
Litany 39
O love, how deep 75
Robed in majesty 134
The Pentecost song 133
You are my witnesses 90

HARVEST
Great is thy faithfulness 78
Harvest of righteousness 69
The seed song 103
Won't you come? 93

Guide to the use of additional instruments

A joyful song – *flute or recorder* 139
Awake, O sleeper – *woodwind
    quartet* 79
Ballad of the dance – *folk-style fiddle
    on refrain* 84
Before the Lord Jehovah's throne –
    counter-melody 13
Blessing and honour – *string
    obligato* 22
Christ the Lord is risen today – *flute
    obligato, bells* 126
Christmas lullaby – *'cello* 140
Fill your heart with love – *harp* 17
Five barley loaves – *verse as counter-
    melody* 98
For you are my God – *trumpet or
    violin obligato* 77
Hosanna, Lord! – *trombone obligato* 132
How much greater – *inner parts* 64
Hymn to the Spirit – *trumpet
    obligato* 142
Jesus, your blood – *melody in
    canon* 25
Jesus shall reign – *trumpet obligato* . . 87
Jubilate Deo – *mandolin* 120
Living Lord – *strings* 83
O for a thousand tongues – *trumpet,
    trombone* 23
O love, how deep – *trumpet
    obligato* 75

Peace, perfect peace – *woodwind
    obligato* 41
Tell my people – *woodwind
    obligato* 50
Tell out, my soul – *trumpet* 19
The bridegroom's song – *trumpet or
    violin* 44
The celebration song – *mandolin* 71
The fishermen – *strings* 56
The instrument song – *various* 105
The sorrow of Mary – *instrumental
    quartet* 128
This, this is the day – *assorted
    percussion* 14
When I survey the wondrous cross –
    violin obligato 28
Worthy the Lamb – *oboe* 29

PERCUSSION
Tambourine
    A joyful song 139
    Alabaré 4
    Clap your hands 16
    God is our Father 109
    Harvest of righteousness *(on
        offbeat)* 69
    O clap your hands 5
    The Lord's my shepherd 111

Castanets, woodsticks
    Arise, shine! 136

I will rejoice 21
¡Resucitó, resucitó! 141

Drums
Children at your feet 66
Christ the worker 108
Jesus is the one who saves 91
Kyrie eleison 92
'Lu-ia, 'lu-ia 53
My Lord, he is a-comin' soon ... 138
Neighbours 88
You are my witnesses 90

Handbells
Come, Holy Ghost (on occasional
    harmony notes) 125
Dona nobis pacem 131
Hymn of glory (on bars 3, 6,
    10) 11
Praise, my soul, the King of heaven
    (on latter part of descant) 18
Xylophone, glockenspiel
Jesus, name above all names ... 34
The seed song 103
When the Lord came 95

The following songs could be used as piano solos:

Abba, Father 104
All the riches of his grace 30
Christmas lullaby 140
His name is wonderful 35
Jesus my Saviour 26
Lord, give us your Spirit 52
Praise God for the body 61

Psalm 84 124
Rain song 106
Sing unto the Lord 116
The celebration song 71
The Lord's prayer 63
There's a river of praise 15
Thy lovingkindness 119
Trust in the Lord 43

Concerning the use of the organ:

The majority of accompaniments in this volume have been written for piano; however, a large number of songs are particularly suited to the addition of the organ as an accompanying instrument. Some part songs (or refrain in parts) may be played as printed: e.g. Fear not, for I have redeemed you; For you are my God; You are my witnesses. Other songs with distinctively pianistic accompaniments need to be adapted to the idiom of the organ: e.g. Alleluia, he is coming; Hymn of glory; Israel, rely on Yahweh; Robed in majesty; The Pentecost song; We are coming, Lord.

Notes for Guitarist/Accompanist

Underlined chords (Em) indicate one strum per bar.

Chords with a slash (E/B) indicate the bass note to be played where a bass instrument is available (e.g. 'E' chord with a 'B' bass note).

'D tuning' involves retuning the strings to achieve different chord patterns. 'Psalm 84' and 'I will lift up my soul' each use a different 'D tuning', as indicated at the top of each song.

Chords marked with an asterisk(*) indicate unusual or non-standard fingering. Fingering charts for these chords are included at the end of each song.

A more delicate texture may be achieved by 'plucking' (playing one or two strings at a time) rather than 'strumming' the accompaniment. Songs that are especially suited to this type of accompaniment are: Bethlehem song, Christmas lullaby, Fill your heart with love, Rain song, The servant song.

Discography

The following songs are available on Fisherfolk recordings

Song Title	*Album*
All the riches of his grace	Celebrate the Whole of It
Alleluia, he is coming	Fisherfolk – Cry Hosanna
Awake, awake to love and work	O for a Thousand Tongues
Ballad of the dance	Fisherfolk – Cry Hosanna
Be like your Father	Be Like Your Father
Children at your feet	God, Make Us Your Family
Christmas lullaby	Wake Up!
Clap your hands	Be Like Your Father
Come, Lord Jesus	Be Like Your Father
Fear not, for I have redeemed you	Celebrate the Whole of It
Fill my cup, Lord	Fisherfolk – Cry Hosanna
Fill your heart with love	Rejoice with the Fisherfolk
Five barley loaves	Sing the Word
For you are my God	Rejoice with the Fisherfolk
Gift of finest wheat	Fisherfolk – Cry Hosanna
God is for me	Fisherfolk – Cry Hosanna
God is our Father	Be Like Your Father
Good morning, Jesus	This is the day
Harvest of righteousness	God, Make Us Your Family
He's able	Wake Up!
Hosanna, Lord!	Be Like Your Father
I will arise and go to Jesus	O for a Thousand Tongues
Jerusalem is fair	O for a Thousand Tongues
Jesus is our King	Fisherfolk – Cry Hosanna
Jesus loves me	Hey Kids, Do You Love Jesus?
Jesus, name above all names	Be Like Your Father
Jesus shall reign	O for a Thousand Tongues
Jesus, you're a wonder	Wake Up!
Jesus, your blood	This is the day
Jubilate Deo	Sing the Word/
	God, Make Us Your Family
Kyrie eleison	Ah! There's the Celebration/
	This is the day
Lo! he comes	Lo! He Comes
'Lu-ia, 'lu-ia	God, Make Us Your Family
My Lord, he is a-comin' soon	Fisherfolk – Cry Hosanna
Neighbours	Fisherfolk– Cry Hosanna

O clap your hands	Fisherfolk – Cry Hosanna
O for a thousand tongues	O for a Thousand Tongues
Praise God for the body	Celebrate the Whole of It
Psalm 8	Rejoice with the Fisherfolk
Psalm 84	On Tiptoe
Rain song	Hey Kids, Do You Love Jesus?/
	Be Like Your Father
Robed in majesty	Fisherfolk – Cry Hosanna
Sing to our Father	Be Like Your Father
The celebration song	Celebrate the Whole of It/
	Ah! There's the Celebration
The fishermen	Love Divine
The instrument song	Wake Up!
The Lord is present	Rejoice with the Fisherfolk
The Lord's my shepherd	Be Like Your Father
The Lord's prayer	Ah! There's the Celebration
The seed song	God, Make Us Your Family
The servant song	Fisherfolk – Cry Hosanna
There's a river of praise	Be Like Your Father
There's a wideness in God's mercy	Love Divine
There's new life in Jesus	This is the day
They that wait upon the Lord	This is the day
This, this is the day	This is the day
We want to bless you	Fisherfolk – Cry Hosanna
When I survey the wondrous cross	Lo! He Comes
When led by the Spirit	Fisherfolk – Cry Hosanna
Whosoever will	Wake Up!
Won't you come?	God, Make Us Your Family
You are my witnesses	God, Make Us Your Family
Your love is changing the world	Fisherfolk – Cry Hosanna

Fisherfolk– Cry Hosanna album to be released September 1980

Index of titles and first lines

The first line of a song is included, in italic type, only where it differs from the title

A joyful song 139
Abba, Father 104
Alabaré 4
All glory to the Father of life 91
All the riches of his grace 30
Allelu, 'lu-ia, 'lu-ia 53
*Alleluia! Alleluia! Opening our
   hearts to him* 55
Alleluia, he is coming 36
Arise, shine! 136

At the cross her station keeping 128
Awake, awake to love and work 48
Awake, O sleeper 79

Ballad of the dance 84
Be like your Father 67
Before the Lord Jehovah's throne ... 13
Before thy throne, O God 135
*Behold, the darkness shall cover the
   earth* 136

Bethlehem song 137
Bless the holy name of Jesus 32
Blessing and honour 22
Bridegroom's song, The 44
Broken for me 68
Brother, let me be your servant 70
But I say unto you 67

Celebration song, The 71
Children at your feet 66
Christ the Lord is risen today 126
Christ the worker 108
Christmas lullaby 140
Clap your hands 16
Come and bless the Lord 121
Come, Holy Ghost 125
Come, Lord Jesus 47
Come! won't you come 93
Come, ye sinners, poor and needy . . . 40
Cradle rocking, cattle lowing 140

Dona nobis pacem 131

Everybody song 86

Falling, falling, gently falling 106
Fear not, for I have redeemed you . . 49
Fear of the Lord, The 42
Fill my cup, Lord 45
Fill your heart with love 17
Fishermen, The 56
Five barley loaves 98
For our life together, we celebrate . . 71
For you are my God 77

Gift of finest wheat 59
Gloria, Gloria, Gloria 12
Glory hallelujah! 11
God is for me 100
God is our Father 109
Good evening, Father 62
Good morning, Jesus 6
Good morning, this is the day 127
Great is thy faithfulness 78

Hallelujah, for the Lord our God 24
Hallelujah! Hallelujah! He is Lord . . 7
Hallelujah . . . our God reigns 24
Hallelujah song 7
Harvest of righteousness 69
He who supplies seed to the sower . . . 69
He's able 73
Here he comes, robed in majesty 134
Here we are, Lord 66
Hiney mah tov 58
His name is wonderful 35
Hosanna, Lord! 132
Hosanna to the living King! 96

*How beautiful the morning and the
    day* 1
How great thou art 80
How lovely is thy dwelling place 124
How much greater 64
Hymn of glory 11
Hymn to the Spirit 142

*I know not why God's wondrous
    grace* 81
I know whom I have believed 81
I lift up my soul 122
*I looked up and I saw my Lord
    a-coming* 36
I will arise and go to Jesus 40
I will dwell in his secret place 117
I will pour out my Spirit 133
*I will praise the Lord with harp and
    string* 96
I will rejoice 21
I will sing of the mercies 76
In the little town of Bethlehem 137
In the presence of your people 20
Instrument song, The 105
Iona Gloria 12
Israel, rely on Yahweh 113

Jerusalem is fair 72
Jesu, Jesu, fill us with your love 88
Jesus 27
Jesus came 38
Jesus is Lord, alleluia 33
Jesus is our King 55
Jesus is the one who saves 91
Jesus ioves me 107
Jesus my Saviour 26
Jesus, name above all names 34
Jesus shall reign 87
Jesus, you're a wonder 31
Jesus, your blood 25
Jubilate Deo 120
Jubilate Deo *(round)* 10
Jubilate, everybody 118

Kyrie eleison 92

Let us praise the Lord with guitar . . . 105
Lift up your heads 123
Like the woman at the well 45
Litany 39
Living Lord 83
Lo! he comes 130
Look around you; can you see? 92
Lord, give us your Spirit 52
Lord is my light, The 112
Lord is my shepherd, The 114
Lord is present, The 8

Lord Jesus Christ, you have come to us 83
Lord's my shepherd, The 111
Lord's prayer, The 63
Love you, love you, Abba, Father ... 104
'Lu-ia, 'lu-ia 53

Man of sorrows................... 129
Morning Psalm 1
My hope is built 82
My Lord, he is a-comin' soon 138
My sheep hear my voice 60

Neighbours 88

O clap your hands 5
O for a thousand tongues 23
O Lord, my God, when I in awesome wonder 80
O Lord, our God, we lift up our hearts to you 39
O Lord, our Lord, how great is your name in the earth 110
O Lord, your love is changing the world 94
O love, how deep 75
Oh, be joyful in the Lord 120
On Christ the solid rock 82
One must water, one must weed 103
Our Father in heaven 63

Peace, perfect peace 41
Pentecost song, The 133
People of God 57
Peter and James and John 101
Praise God for the body 61
Praise, my soul, the King of heaven 18
Praise ye the Lord 3
Psalm 8 110
Psalm 84 124
Pure light....................... 51

Rain song 106
¡Resucitó, resucitó! 141
Robed in majesty 134

Seed song, The 103
Servant song, The 70
Silent night 97
Sing a song, a joyful song 139
Sing to our Father 9

Sing unto the Lord 116
Sorrow of Mary, The 128
Sound on the trumpet............. 44
Spirit, working in creation 142

Tell my people 50
Tell out, my soul 19
The bridegroom's song 44
The celebration song 71
The fear of the Lord 42
The fishermen.................... 56
The instrument song 105
The Lord is my light.............. 112
The Lord is my shepherd 114
The Lord is present 8
The Lord's my shepherd 111
The Lord's prayer 63
The Pentecost song 133
The seed song 103
The servant song 70
The sorrow of Mary 128
There's a new song in the land 54
There's a quiet understanding 37
There's a river of praise........... 15
There's a wideness in God's mercy .. 89
There's new life in Jesus 99
They cast their nets in Galilee 56
They that wait upon the Lord....... 46
This, this is the day 14
Those who trust in the Lord 115
Thy lovingkindness 119
To you, Yahweh, I lift up my soul ... 122
Trust in the Lord 43

We are coming, Lord 65
We cry, 'Hosanna, Lord' 132
We must follow the Lord 102
We want to bless you 2
When I survey the wondrous cross .. 28
When led by the Spirit............ 85
When the Lord came 95
Who does Jesus love? 86
Whosoever will................... 74
Won't you come? 93
Worthy the Lamb 29

You are my witnesses 90
You satisfy the hungry heart 59
Your love is changing the world..... 94